The Character Jug Collectors Handbook

by

Kevin Pearson N

G000144299

Published in the United Kingdom by
Kevin Francis Publishing
Landcroft House, 85 Landcroft Road, East Dulwich, London SE22 9JS

Typeset by
E J Folkard, Crayford, Kent DA1 3QF

Printed in England by
The Greenwich Press, London SE7

Photographs
Trevor Leak, Dick Nicholson, Syd Gardner, Phillips, Ruth Pollard, Derek and Jean, Christies, Louis Taylors, Royal Doulton Collectors Club, Barry Weiss, Doulton Direct, Venta File, Tom Power.

Acknowledgements
Francis Salmon, Tom Power, Louise Irvine, John, Derek and Jean, Gossland Collectibles, Yesterdays, DSW, James Scannell.

Cover
Francis Salmon.

Important Notice
All the information and valuations have been compiled from reliable sources and every effort has been made to eliminate errors and questionable data. Nevertheless the possibility of error always exists. The publisher and author will not be held responsible for losses which may occur in the purchase, sale or other transaction of items because of information contained herein. Readers who feel they have discovered errors are invited to WRITE and inform us so that these may be corrected in subsequent editions.

Products listed or shown were originally manufactured by Royal Doulton Limited. Kevin Pearson is an independent publisher who is in no way connected with Royal Doulton Ltd, which claim and reserve all rights under the trademark and copyright laws with respect to each of the products listed or shown. The products are listed or shown with the permission of Royal Doulton. The prices are those of the author and not necessarily endorsed by Royal Doulton.

Additional Copies
Further copies of this book can be obtained by ordering direct from Kevin Francis Publishing, Landcroft House, 85 Landcroft Road, East Dulwich, London SE22 9JS.

Any reader who wishes to contact the author for further information on character jugs should write via the publisher's address.

Fifth Edition
Kevin Francis Publishing

©1992 K. J. Pearson

CONTENTS

Scaramouche First Version

THE DISCONTINUED CHARACTER JUG MARKET

A discontinued character jug is one that is no longer offered for sale by Royal Doulton. It may have been withdrawn from the current line to make way for new models, or it may be a limited edition which has now been sold out. In the last twenty years a complex and sophisticated collectors market for discontinued character jugs has developed. Thousands of collectors and the dealers who serve them have joined in the search for character jugs around the world.

Tony Weller

The Beefeater

The growing demand, coupled with a limited supply, has created a market worth more than a million pounds a year, with very rare jugs selling for tens of thousands of pounds. Character jugs with an original price of £1 in the 1960s now bring £500, whilst prototypes from the 1940s bought for a few shillings can be worth over £20000.

Of course the same applies to the 'overseas' market. Character jugs are collected in the USA, Canada, Australia, New Zealand, South Africa as well as in the UK. The existence of this international market follows the trading pattern of Royal Doulton's exports to the Commonwealth and North America. Today, Doulton dealers from New York may compete with British collectors at auctions in Australia, while Canadian dealers compete with American collectors in London.

A typical character jug could first turn up at a car boot sale in Stafford selling to a local antique dealer for a couple of pounds. He in turn may sell it to another dealer who, knowing a collector in the Midlands will sell it on to him. It could then be used by the collector as a 'trade-in' with a specialised Doulton dealer for a different jug. From there it could pass through several dealers' hands before finally selling at a Doulton fair ending up occupying pride of place in a New York or London collection.

The international aspect of the market has been considerably helped by the development of an official Doulton Collectors Club, started in 1980, with branches in England, North America and Australia and New Zealand. As well as issuing its own limited editions, the club publishes an international magazine for all collectors of Doulton ware.

Discontinued character jugs are sold at auctions, antique fairs, antique shops and Doulton collecting fairs: in fact anywhere connected with art and antiques; such is their present status. The market is very active and constantly changing as certain jugs move in and out of fashion.

The lifeblood of any market is an increase in demand from new collectors. Every year new collectors catch the bug and the underlying strength of the market is that a great number of these new collectors have developed into long term enthusiasts, with many collecting for 30 years — and others ten or fifteen.

Although people have been buying and collecting character jugs since they were first introduced in 1934, the discontinued market only started to take shape in the USA in the early 1970s. It very quickly spread to the UK as American dealers, eager to acquire stock, started to buy overseas and found themselves competing with British collectors — collectors who had always been there but who now found themselves having to compete quite hard against the American dollar.

At this stage there was very little knowledge as to rarity. There were no printed records of production periods and very little to go on in the way of experience as only a few 'second hand' jugs were appearing in the market. Collectors were buying jugs at prices that bore little relation to the scarcity of the jug — the truly golden days of collecting where an 'Arry fetched the same price as a Pearly Boy.

Although the publication of Desmond Eyles' book, Good Sir Toby in 1956

The Gardener, First Version

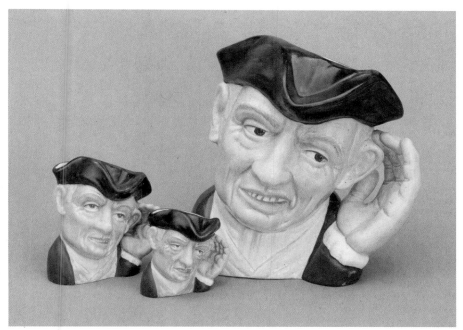

'Ard of 'Earing

helped popularise Doulton character jugs, it did little to promote the discontinued market; the reason being the relatively low number of jugs discontinued. By 1960, the large number of withdrawals meant that the book was already out of date.

In 1976, Richard Dennis published the booklet, Doulton Character Jugs which, for the first time, gave collectors some idea of the scope their collection could achieve.

A great boost to the market occurred in 1978 with Richard Dennis's publication of Doulton Character and Toby Jugs, written by Desmond Eyles. Collectors could for the first time identify most of the discontinued character jugs, and the production dates given created the first awareness of rarity. The market quickly began to gather pace in the late 1970s as collectors started to embark on building a comprehensive collection, the initial intention of many being to acquire every jug listed in the book.

The value of short-run production jugs as identified in the book was re-appraised. Collectors became increasingly focused on the concept of rarity, several jugs quickly becoming the preserve of a few unless a lucky collector was fortunate enough to find one cheaply: a situation which was highly likely as, to the uninitiated, a £10 jug looks much the same as a £10000 jug.

In 1986, Jocelyn Lukins published her book, *Collecting Royal Doulton Character and Toby Jugs*, providing a welcome pocket-size guide to all the character jugs known. Such was the popularity of character jugs and the need for information that a second edition of the book was published in 1989.

The early 1980s had seen a continued growth in the market with collector groups forming in several countries and the introduction of two separate newsletters in California and Canada with subscribers across the world. Australia has had its own Toby Jug Collecting society since 1982 and there is a flourishing collectors club in New Zealand.

During this period a consensus with regard to value started to form. The first American price guide from Barry Weiss appeared in the early 1980s and my own American and English guide appeared in 1984. The price guides served to expand the market further as new collectors were encouraged. Such was the interest that the price guides appeared yearly in an attempt to keep up with the market.

All the UK major auction houses started to hold Doulton auctions where character jugs were strongly featured. Auctioneers such as Phillips of London deemed Doulton important enough to appoint a full-time Doulton specialist.

The first 'Doulton Only' collectors fair featuring character jugs took place in Oberlin, Ohio in 1980. Over 1000 collectors attended and the event was a great success.

The first British Doulton Fair was held in the Park Lane Hotel, London in 1982 and has been held there annually ever since. In 1985, the first International Doulton Fair was held 15 miles from the Royal Doulton potteries in Stafford. With 70 exhibitors from the USA, UK, Australia and Canada and over 2000 collectors attending, some from as far afield as Saudi Arabia, the international Doulton market had come of age.

The Beatles (including John Lennon Colourway)

At the present time the UK has two fairs a year, one in London the other in Stafford. The USA has four fairs a year and Canada, one. Some specialist dealers attend all the fairs around the world.

Rarity has always been the factor which has determined prices, i.e. how long ago was a character jug made and what sort of quantities was it made in? Age is a secondary aspect: a Cavalier made in 1940 may only bring £85 when sold whilst an 'Ard of 'Earing made in 1967 could bring £700. The difference lies in the three year production lifetime of the 'Ard of 'Earing as compared to the 20 year production run of the Cavalier.

The same holds true for limited editions. The lower the edition size, the greater the eventual appreciation as new collectors entering the market find fewer examples available.

Mr Quaker

Although Doulton's policy has been to keep all editions to 5000, this is not always the case. In earlier days some editions designed for promotional use, such as advertising commissions, were far smaller and consequently failed to take into account collector demand. The few jugs that were allocated for collectors were greatly oversubscribed and the value went through the roof. A good example of this is Mr Quaker, introduced in 1985 in an edition of 3500 for promotional uses by Quaker Oats, with only a few hundred for collectors. Two weeks after release the jug was changing hands on the market for over eight times its issue price!

Supply is the main factor, but there are others which determine value. The sheer range of jugs available naturally means that there are some jugs which are more appealing than others. Whilst appeal can vary from one person to another there are jugs which most collectors prefer over others and this can be a factor in any valuation. Such a preference distorts the demand for the jug and consequently raises the price. A good example is the Gardener character jug which, since its withdrawal in 1981, along with several other jugs of equal production runs, has consistently outperformed the other jugs by three to one. The Gardener seems to have universal appeal amongst collectors and the value has been bid up accordingly.

The relative exchange rate between markets can have a significant effect. In 1988, the UK market slowed down considerably as the value of the dollar rose, pricing many Americans out of the English market.

Special circumstances can also play a part. In 1988 I was attending the Miami Doulton Fair, held in January each year. Part of my job was to promote our commissioned charity jug, The Collector. It was decided that we would auction for charity the very first example of the jug to be sold in the USA. We signed and numbered the jug 'USA 1' on its base. Apart from this added marketing element there was nothing to distinguish the jug from the other 4999 of the edition. I had expected to raise $350 for the jug which would have been nearly twice its retail value. We had, however, underestimated the demand for the jug.

The auction commenced immediately after the collectors' banquet held on the Saturday evening. Using a spoon as a makeshift gavel I nervously opened the bidding at $150 to be immediately reassured as a lady on my left took up the bid. I then proceeded to move the bidding up by $20 stages with bids coming fast and furiously from the floor. When it reached £350 a bid of $500.00 was called out by an English dealer. Everyone went silent for a second before bidding quickly restarted. Buoyed by this leap in the bidding I increased each bid by $50 and still the hands went up. The bidding slowed down at $750 and the only two people left contesting the jug were a dealer from New Orleans and a local collector. At $750 the bid was with the collector until the dealer raised it to $800. The strain was beginning to tell on both parties and there was a deadly hush around the hall. Just as I was about to bring my spoon down on the $800 the collector took a deep breath and bid $850. It was enough, the first Collector jug in the USA sold for $850.

At the end of the day the true value of any character jug is that which an individual collector is prepared to pay for it. Each decision is made on its own merits and reflect the personal situation of that individual as well as the market. Collectors should be aware of this when deciding upon the acquisition of any new piece. Just because a jug fetched £100 at auction does

The Trapper

Simon the Cellarer

not mean it is worth £100 if sold privately. As well as considering the actual desire of both the buyer and seller, attention must be paid to such factors as the 15% auction commission and the circumstances on the day at the saleroom. The price could simply be a reflection of personal competition between two dealers or collectors.

The opportunity of a bargain has always been a powerful attraction for collectors and the early sales pattern of Doulton china ensured that one could turn up literally anywhere. Every collector I know has a story to tell and it is gratifying to find that even in these knowledgeable days the bargains are still to be found.

The collector who purchased for £70 a Pearly Girl during the afternoon at an Antique fair, who then turned down an offer of £4000 from a dealer who had been standing at the fair and had not spotted the jug, acts as an inspiration to collectors everywhere.

My favourite story is of the man who, in 1949, was given a character jug by his mother along with one for each of his three brothers. Each jug related to the personality of each brother and his, with its painted face, was viewed as a happy clown — just like his. The jug was not in fact a Clown but the pilot Maori which never went into production. His brothers' jugs, which included Simon the Cellarer for the drinker amongst them, were made for over 20 years. The happy ending to the story is that the jug survived the war and the next 40 years with its owner until 1988 when, after seeing a price guide, he sold it for £14000 and built a new extension to his house on the proceeds. This has been the only example found in the past ten years. If another was found I would expect it to bring over £20000.

With over 300 different jugs available it is only the dedicated few who possess both the inclination and cheque book to acquire a complete collection. The great bulk of collectors tend to collect a particular size or type of character jug. Many concentrate on areas such as derivatives or characters from series such as Williamsburg.

Those with very large collections who find that all there is left in new characters is the virtually unobtainable pilot jugs, start to move towards more unusual variations — such as special backstamps, white character jugs and colourways and their variations.

There are many promotional backstamps to be found on character jugs from the 1930s and the commissions of the 1980s. Some, such as Salt River Cement Works, are very rare and when found being near to £1000.

White character jugs which are unpainted but glazed bring, as a general rule, 10% more than their coloured counterparts despite the fact that they are invariably damaged, being seconds. Several collectors are now in the process of trying to complete a collection comprised solely of white jugs and there are undoubtedly unknown white jugs to be found. I am in little doubt than they too will be bid up by several hundred percent due to their rarity.

Between 1968 and 1971 character jugs were produced in bone china. Slightly smaller than their earthenware counterparts and with a translucent base, these jugs are prized in their own right and there are several collectors who will only buy bone china jugs.

With the long history of character jugs and the nature of the hand painted production process, topics like colourways and colour variations could justify a book on their own. Suffice to say that the colourways can happen by accident or as part of the eventual trial process. Their relative value depends upon the scale of change and noticeable difference to the jug. Thereby a minor change such as a Mae West with no eyebrows will have no added value while a difference such as the Henry VIII second that is missing all the on-glaze red colouring is worth a considerable premium. The latter were sold through a few UK retail outlets as a half price second for £12.00 each. The first example discovered in 1986 sold for £3000 although since then many more have turned up and the value has fallen back, they still bring over £500 on the market.

That, then, is the discontinued Doulton market — an international enthusiasm for jugs that shows no sign of abating and every sign of continuing to develop and expand in the years to come. The jugs of today are without doubt the heirlooms of tomorrow and in this collecting world tomorrow is often only a few years away.

Mae West

MARKET REPORT — Better days ahead

Welcome to the fifth edition of the Collector's Handbook. It's now seven years since the first edition of my book was published and these seven years have seen many fluctuations in the collectors market which at times seems to have emulated a roller coaster of epic proportions.

The last two years has seen a sensible re-appraisal of the market. There have been several high price casualties among the rarer jugs which have not held their values (white and red hair clowns), while amongst the lower end of the market the early eighties discontinuations have powered ahead.

I think it is true to say that current trends have taken this re-appraisal into account and that prices generally are recovering. Prices have bottomed out and in many cases are starting to move ahead although not at quite the same rate that has been seen in the past. Whatever the state of market confidence, certain jugs are truly rare and any new collector entering the market (and there are many) will have to compete hard to secure certain pieces.

Part of the reason for the stagnation in prices is, I believe, a result of Royal Doulton's manipulation of the market. In an attempt to cash in on the burgeoning market for discontinued character jugs, the manufacturers created a number of 'colourway' and 'special backstamp' editions. Whereas such novelties were inadvertently produced by Doulton in the past, making them highly collectable, the collectors now found themselves being manipulated. For example, the Mad Hatter was discontinued in 1983 but, after a growing secondary market for the jug, Royal Doulton re-introduced it in a new colourway, limited edition. Thus began the stirrings of collector uncertainty. When new 'limited editions' were brought out and snapped up by collectors, they were to find that the limit was a colourway only — the jug was afterwards incorporated into the character jug range. Similarly with backstamps. Normally the preserve of the advertising industry, these backstamps were now nothing other than 'gimmicks' for sales.

The last year has thus seen a downturn in the collector response to new editions and colourways. This has been reflected in the reduction of the lower number limit of 5000 in edition size to 1500 and less for backstamp editions.

It may now well be that the development of special commissions and new colourways has run its course. There seem to be far fewer plans now for commissions, which is welcome. It is almost certain that those new commissions likely to succeed will only be those that are original (i.e. not a colourway or backstamp issue) and those that have a realistic edition size. By realistic I mean 2000 or under, the time of 5000 editions is now well past its time.

The problems caused by the policies of Royal Doulton and their effect upon prices have been compounded by the publicity given to character jugs and the subsequent discovery and sale of character jugs by the general public. If three and four years ago we had a seller's market, the last two years have certainly been a buyer's market. Dealers now regularly turn down collections while in the past these would have been snapped up and quickly resold.

What then for the future? Things have certainly changed and the next few years should be quite interesting. It seems the number of special commissions and their issue size is set to fall. The increasing price rises for current ware in the last couple of years must surely be over now as they have doubled in price over the last three years. Given that these two assumptions are true I feel that the next two years should bring about an encouraging growth in the market. I think those jugs which are established as being truly rare will appreciate significantly, especially the ten 1960s withdrawals such as Gulliver and 'Ard of 'Earing which continue to be very difficult to find.

The market has certainly undergone a re-appraisal and can now be seen as entering a mature phase. Those still left in the market are now far more discriminating and I think this will be reflected in more consideration being given in terms of quality. This seems to be recognised by Royal Doulton who have considerably improved the quality of new releases which I think has gone some way to stem the flow from the market.

The unprecedented number of withdrawals in 1992 (105 jugs) should act as a boost to the market. Certain jugs such as the Witch which were only in production for six months should do very well indeed.

To summarize, as indicated by the title of this section, the worst is almost certainly over and I now look to the future with a lot more confidence. Collectors should still be very careful with regard to price and the same old rules about shopping around etc still apply, but on the whole I think anyone seeking to expand their collection should be able to purchase with confidence as I think it is very unlikely that we will see further price falls and indeed I think the reverse is now the case.

The Mikado

How to Use This Book

This book, as well as being a source of information on discontinued character jugs, is also designed to enable collectors to keep accurate records of their collection. There are two quick reference lists for current and discontinued jugs. In addition to this, all the discontinued jugs are given a further listing in the market value section. In this section each jug is listed with its individual details in the manner shown below:

Clark Gable Designer S. Taylor

Once asked by a magazine writer:
"How does it feel to be the screen's greatest lover?"
The five-times-married Hollywood star replied:
"It's a living."

This jug was withdrawn due to copyright problems. Less than 500 are known to exist.

Size	D.Nos	Production Dates	£	Market Values $	Date Acquired	Price Paid	
Large	6709	1984	£1500-£2000	$3000-$4000	_____	_____	☐

The boxed space can be ticked to indicate the purchase of a character jug, the date and amount paid to be written in the lined space. This should help collectors avoid buying duplicates by accident, as well as providing a record of their collection. The market value listed for each character jug is intended as a guide only; the actual value put on a jug rests with the collector. There are several blank pages at the end of this book which will be useful for notes. Collectors may find it useful to use these pages for recording auction dates and dealer's telephone numbers or other relevant notes.

Ugly Duchess

Walrus & Carpenter

The North American Market

The North American discontinued Doulton market (comprising the USA and Canada) is distinctly different to that of the UK. When one considers that Great Britain could be comfortably dropped into one of the Great Lakes, one of the reasons for the difference is readily apparent. The sheer size of North America has resulted in the discontinued Doulton market being essentially mail order. Doulton does turn up in antique fairs, flea markets and antique shops in the same way as it does in Britain. However one will not have a great deal of choice unless contact is made with some of the 20 odd specialist Doulton dealers who dominate the North American market. Due to the great distances involved most Doulton dealers use a mailing list for distributing their "for sale and wants" lists amongst collectors. Apart from buying through the post or relying on the occasional "find" the other option is to attend one of the specialist Doulton Fairs which exist in the USA. These fairs run for three days over a weekend starting on a Friday evening. They usually have lectures on aspects of Doulton as well as a timetable of social events.

Ronald Reagan

How Character Jugs are Made

Ever since the first character jugs were issued in the 1930s, Royal Doulton Character Jugs have had a reputation for quality. This could be due to the time consuming nature of the production processes involved.

The original artist first models the selected character in clay, and on the basis of this design, a master mould is made. From this 'master', a second working model is made, which in turn may have up to thirty pouring moulds made from it.

These moulds are only used 25-30 times, ensuring the quality of each individual jug produced. The pouring moulds are used to cast the jug which is then removed and filed down to avoid seams. The handle, which is cast separately, is then stuck to the main body of the jug. The completed jug then undergoes its first firing. After careful inspec-

Modeller Geoff Blower working on the Antique Dealer

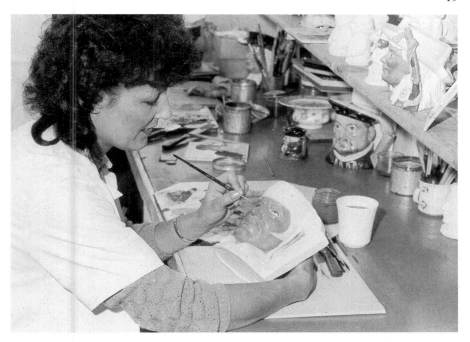

tion to remove any flawed jugs, they are then sent to the decorating studios. At the studios the jugs are hand-painted in the colours indicated in the original design. This is carried out by row upon row of skilled painters. The painted jug is then fired again to harden the colours. They are then dipped in a special solution and fired for the last time to produce the glossy finish. During the late 1960s and early 1970s, some jugs were made of china instead of earthenware and have the translucent appearance of fine china. If these jugs are held up to the light the shadow of any small object such as a pencil is discernible. In the firing process a jug will shrink by up to 12 per cent. The slightly uneven nature of this shrinkage process has resulted in very slight variations in size to jugs of the same character. The fine china jugs are noticeably smaller when compared to earthenware jugs.

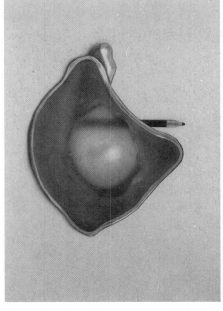

A fine bone china jug with a pencil showing through its opaque base

Professional Restorations

With the value of discontinued character jugs having risen over the past few years, there has been a corresponding rise in the number of professionally restored jugs appearing on the market. Higher prices now make it financially worthwhile to have badly damaged character jugs professionally restored. Many of these restorations are virtually undetectable to the naked eye and are only visible under an ultra-violet lamp. They can be detected by tapping a coin, or similar object, around the side and edges of a jug. If a jug has been restored, the repaired area will give off a slightly different sound and vibration when tapped. Another method is to use one's teeth to bite the jug. The teeth are very sensitive and can pick up on restored glaze because it is not baked at the high temperatures of the original firings. The new glaze is softer than the original glaze even though it appears to be perfect. When the end of the tooth touches a restored section the effect is a dead feeling such as the difference between a hard and soft bar of chocolate. Another method of detection is to stick a pin into the suspected area. If the pin goes in and makes a mark the jug has been restored.

Any reputable dealer will guarantee, if asked, that a jug is perfect and will refund the money if a jug is proved to be a restoration after being purchased. To avoid later misunderstanding it is always wise to ask for this verbal guarantee.

Professional restorations, especially of rare jugs, do have a market value and sell well if priced accordingly. Many collectors will buy a 'good' restoration for their collection. This is done either to reduce the cost of collecting or to enhance the collection until a perfect model of the jug can be found. The price of a restoration depends upon the quality of the restoration; as a general guide expect to pay 50-60% below the market value of a perfect version, although a particularly rare restored jug could fetch 70-80% of its perfect market value.

Those seeking out professional restorers are advised to check the Antique Trade Gazette — a good source for adverts from restorers.

Both these jugs have been extensively restored around the rim

White Jugs

These are uncoloured character jugs, i.e. only part of the glazing process has been carried out. Nearly all the examples found have slight damage, usually underglaze chips or cracks. However perfect examples do turn up.

There are three possible reaons for the existence of whiteware pieces on the Doulton market. From 1945-1952, according to the chairman of Doulton & Co, USA, William Carey, it was official policy, due to rationing regulations on decorated ware, to sell whiteware pieces only on the British market. Since 1952 other whiteware pieces have turned up, usually thought to be factory seconds that have slipped out of the factory. Another theory suggests that some seconds may have been sold to Doulton's employees in the factory shop.

The majority of whiteware jugs date from the 1940s and 1950s, however quite a few examples have dated from the 1960s and 1970s. The earliest examples known date from 1937 which serves to scotch the war theory.

There are collectors who specialise in whiteware. This is a thin market and only certain jugs command a premium against their coloured counterparts.

It is impossible to list these jugs as the market is very thin and a couple of discoveries can have a marked effect on price. In this situation a price guide is useless and the collector has to fall back on the natural source of knowledge, himself! In other words observe and ask to find out what is worth buying.

Trademark Identification and Dating

Each Royal Doulton Character Jug carries the Royal Doulton Lion and Crown backstamp on its base with the character's name, except for tinies, written on the back of the jug. Models may carry a copyright registration date and a D. Number as well. There may be several registration numbers on the base of a jug differing for various countries in which the design has been registered. The only mark on the bottom of a jug which may affect its value if not present is the omission of the Lion and Crown backstamp. The appearance or non-appearance of names, registration dates and D. Numbers does not affect a character jug's value.

Character jugs that have only been in production for a few years can easily be dated from production records. If the jug has been in production over a longer period, the dating process is not so simple. To an experienced collector, the quality and strength of individual colours can be an indication of age. In addition to this, older jugs quite often have a colouring on the lip inside the top of the jug. This practice ceased in the early 1960s. The old versions can also be identified if the base bears the words, 'Reg. applied for', or has only one registered design number. This is the British registration. The first jugs of a new character were always registered and sold in Britain prior to being sold overseas.

Jugs that have their names printed in inverted commas, with or without a registration number, date after the previously mentioned marks. Jugs produced after 1950 have the printed name, D. Number and several registered numbers on their base. Up to the early 1960s character jugs were produced with indented pupils in their eyes. Jugs produced after this period have smooth rounded eyes.

On the base of some jugs there appears an "A" mark, which is a capital letter A printed next to the Doulton trade mark. The A mark appears on a range of Doulton products made between 1939 and 1955. This mark was used only as a factory control mark to direct wares to a certain kiln. It does not appear on all the character jugs made during this period, and it is of little use for the precise dating of a character jug. On the American discontinued character jug market however, the A mark jugs command a slightly higher price than non A mark jugs.

Early character jugs can be precisely dated if there is a printed numeral to the right of the Lion and Crown. This numbering system, which also applies to figures and other items, began with the number 1 in 1928 and ran to number 27 in 1954 but was only applied sporadically. Where they do appear, a simple rule is to add the number to 1927 so a 13 would indicate 1940.

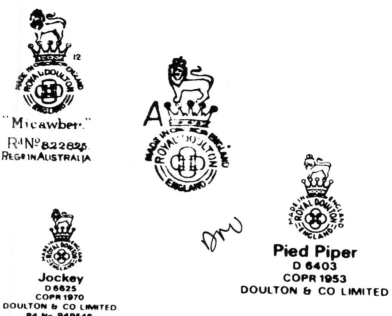

The left hand mark has been scored out to indicate that the jug is a second

The base of the Smuts jug

Character Jug Handle Variations

Handles do exhibit the same diversification, creativity and occasional valuable variations as jugs themselves. The first character jugs produced in the 1930s generally had very plain utilitarian handles. There were exceptions however, Smuts with its springbok's head built into the back of the handle and the Clowns have rich colourful handles, while Simon the Cellarer has a handle in the form of a bunch of keys and Dick Turpin has a gun for a handle. Touchstone, introduced in 1936, has two comic masks built into its handle giving a very pleasant look to the jug. Other early jugs were not so decorative, for example: Mr. Micawber and Mr. Pickwick are amongst other which simply have plain black handles coming out of their side or back. This shortage of good handles amongst the early jugs is well illustrated by the twelve tinies. Although introduced at a later date all the characters in the tinies are amongst the first produced in other sizes. Of the twelve characters used, only two, John Peel with his riding crop and Sairey Gamp with her umbrella had handles which reflected the story behind the character.

The 1950s with the introduction of such jugs as Rip Van Winkle, the Poacher and Don Quixote signalled a start by the Doulton designers to pay greater attention to and exploit the creative potential of character jug handles. The ten 1960s introductions and subsequent withdrawals such as 'Ard of 'Earing with its handle in the form of a cupped hand to his ear and the Ugly Duchess with her flamingo handle are, for my money, some of the most pleasing and interesting of all the 90 odd jugs produced to date. The Ugly Duchess handle is particulary attractive for its artistic style and for also using a bird associated with the Duchess in the classic "Alice in Wonderland" Other jugs have featured animals as handles. Examples are, Captain Ahab's whale, Gone Away's fox, Long John Silver's parrot and St George's dragon to name but a few. Other handles have depicted objects associated with the main character such as the Jockey's winning post, the Mikado's fan,

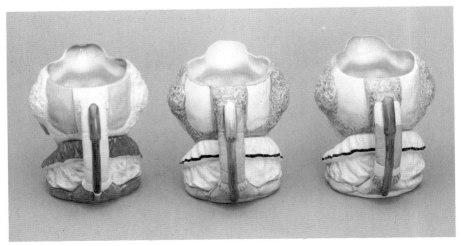

The Clown Handles

the Gondolier's boat and the Gladiator's dagger. The astrological symbols on the Fortune Teller's handle and the Star of David, an old magic symbol on Merlin's handle are examples of associated symbols being used. Quite often a handle will depict more than one object associated with the character; Captain Hook's alligator and clock, Robinson Crusoe's palm tree and Man Friday are examples. An even more intricate design is the Gulliver handle which has two Lilliputians from the story of Gullivers Travels attempting to lift a hair from the jugs head.

From these and other examples of handles we can see the creative potential possible in character jug handles. Once one has settled on the main design for a jug there are endless handle variations possible, a fact recently exploited by designer Michael Abberley in his Santa Claus character jug.

Reindeer and Doll handle Santa Claus

There are in a few cases slight variations in the handles of the same jugs, several of which make a great difference to the value. Anne of Cleves is a good example of this. The handle of this jug is in the shape of a horse. Early versions in 1980 had the horse's ears upright, sticking out from its head. Due to an unacceptably high percentage of ears breaking off during transit, the ears were remodelled to be flat on the horse's head. This early version now commands a premium price from collectors seeking to acquire it.

A similar situation occurred with the miniature size Old Salt. First introduced in the large and small size in 1961, the jug has a handle in the form of a mermaid. Her outside arm is raised with her hand holding the back of her head and a noticeable space in the crook of her arm. When the miniature size was introduced in 1983, this space was no longer present because of similar problems caused during firing, i.e the arm kept snapping off. However, a limited number were apparently piloted with the space in the crook of her arm still present; these occasionally do turn up and are avidly sought after by collectors.

The Beefeater jug has a rich variety of handles. First introduced in 1947 the back of the handle carried the initials 'GR' George Rex, signifying the Beefeater's status as a member of the royal household of King George. When Queen Elizabeth Regina, ascended the throne in 1953, the initials were changed to 'ER' Elizabeth Regina, representing the new monarch. No doubt when Prince Charles ascends the throne the jug, if still produced, will change its initials once again to 'CR' Charles Rex. The early 'GR' version does command a slightly higher value than the current 'ER' version. In addition to the initial variation, there also exists another version known as the gold handle Beefeater. In this version the handle is very colourful with an intricate gold thread pattern on it. Needless to say, this version is very valuable and highly sought after.

Other handle variations which do not make too much difference to value also exist. John Barleycorn, the first character jug ever produced, has a very plain handle which does not depict any aspect of the jug's character. It is possible to identify early versions of the jug by a slight difference in the handle; the later version has both ends of the handle stuck to the side of the jug while the early versions have the top end of the handle disappearing into the top of the jug. Sairey Gamp has in early large versions an S etched at the bottom of its handle. John Peel's handle, in the form of hunting crop, has a coloured band just below the corner of the handle. Two colours were used, orange and grey, the grey being the more common of the two, yet no real difference in value exists between the two versions. Another interesting variation occurs in the John Doulton jug issued by the Collectors Club; the clock face incorporated into the handle either reads 2 o'clock or 8 o'clock. Collectors who have the 8 o'clock version are founder members of the Club, whilst those with the 2 o'clock version joined at later date. The time was apparently changed after the launch period.

The latest and one of the best uses yet of handles is the new Henry VIII character jug released in 1991. This twin handled limited edition jug is a superb example of the handle potential of character jugs. A sentiment echoed and proved worldwide, where it sold out on release and won the British Collectable Award at the London Collectors Showcase Fair 1991.

Henry VIII, Second Version

Special Backstamps

Over the last year there has been a considerable growth in collecting some of the more unusual backstamps which appear. These are usually advertising or promotional messages added to the base above or below the lion and crown Doulton mark. These jugs are relatively scarce and difficult to obtain and few were actually produced.

Printed Character Names

Several of the early jugs produced by Royal Doulton had the name of the character printed on the base. This occurs on jugs dating from the 1940s such as the Fat Boy. However, the prescence of a character's name on its base, while being an indication of an early example, does not necessarily add to the value of a jug. Additional words on the base such as the rhyme on the base of Mephistopheles will add to the value of the jug.

This growth in the popularity of backstamps, along with other variations, has led to some sharp increases in their value. At the present time, unusual backstamps can considerably enhance the value of a character jug. It is difficult to give precise values as the market in backstamps is relatively thin.

A very rare commission backstamp

City of Stoke Jubilee Year

Painted on a number of jugs presented to a working committee, the backstamp reads; "With the compliments of Lord Mayor & Lady Mayoress, Alderman Harold Clowes, O.B.E., J.P. and Miss Christine Clowes".

Canadian Centennial

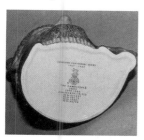

Three large size jugs carry the words 'Canadian Centennial Series 1867-1967'. These were issued in Canada in 1967 to celebrate 100 years of independence. Not surprisingly all the characters are North Americans. Although they were not officially released in the UK there seem to be many to be found which seems to indicate that several must have been sold in this country.

Character	Market Values	
Trapper	£90-£110	$300-$400
Lumberjack	£90-£110	$300-$400
North American Indian	£90-£110	$300-$400

American Express

These are two jugs which were first issued in 1982 as part of the forthcoming Celebrity Collection. They were initially only available through American Express in the USA with a special backstamp which reads: 'Premier Edition for American Express'.

Character	Number Issued	Market Value
W. C. Fields	1500	Not known in UK
	(900)	$300-$400
Mae West	500	Not known in UK
	(300)	$700-$800

Darley & Son

These small size jugs were produced in the 1920s for two department stores in Sheffield and Rotherham. They are overprinted on the base with the words 'Souvenir from Darley & Son Sheffield and Rotherham'. There may well be other characters with the same backstamp that have not yet been found.

Character	Market Values	
Tony Weller	£200–£250	$500–$700
Parson Brown	£200–£250	$500–$700
Jester	£200–£250	$500–$700

Bentalls

There are two versions of their backstamp which appear on several small size jugs and a few large size. The first reads 'Souvenir from Bentalls Jubilee Year 1935'. Known characters are: Old Charley, Parson Brown, Sairey Gamp and Tony Weller.
The second version reads 'Souvenir from Bentalls 1936'. Known small size characters in this group are The Jester, Simon the Cellarer, Tony Weller and Dick Turpin. A large size John Barleycorn and Nelson have also been found with this backstamp.
Market value all characters £200-£250 $500-$600

Winston Churchill Toby

All three sizes of this jug can be found with the addition of the words "Prime Minister of Great Britain — 1940 —" These extra words date the jug from the 1940s or 1950s. Their presence will add to the value of this current jug by at least 50 per cent.

Michael Doulton Signature

Not a backstamp but the actual signature of Michael Doulton at one of the many collectors evenings he attends. Although appreciated by collectors the presence of this signature does not add to the value of a jug.

Coleman's Compliments

This backstamp has been found on a small number of large Farmer John character jugs, a Paddy tobacco jar and a large John Barleycorn. From the date of these jugs we can assume they were advertising pieces produced for Coleman's sauces in the 1930s. Their rarity has prevented a price structure developing but they are certainly worth more than the Bentalls jugs. The exact value will of course be up to the collector who is fortunate enough to purchase an example. An example sold at Phillips in October 1986 for £700.

Salt River Cement Works

Found on a large John Barleycorn and a Paddy tobacco jar, this stamp shows 'WITH COM-

PLIMENTS — FROM — SALT RIVER CEMENT WORKS' in a large circle around the standard Doulton trademark. As with the Coleman's jugs a value is difficult to determine but would certainly be above the other backstamps.

Lord Nelson

In 1955 three Nelsons were produced with commemorative backstamps of the 150th Anniversary of the Battle of the Trafalgar. These were for the Admiralty Room in Whitehall and were designated "First Lord", "First Sea Lord" and "Secretary" respectively. They were intended to be held in perpetuity for use by the holders of those offices. Another example of Lord Nelson with no office title was made for display at the Victory Museum at HM Dockyard, Portsmouth. Seven additional jugs were presented to a Russian Naval Squadron in 1955. The "Secretary" jug found its way on the market in 1985 and sold for an undisclosed sum.

The Tinies

There are at least four variations in backstamp marks with some six characters, Paddy, Old Charley, Fat Boy, Sairey Gamp, Sam Weller and Mr Micawber carrying the names of their characters. In a few rarer cases the name is also found along the shoulders of the jugs.

Griffiths Pottery House
The Fireman

Three slight variations of backstamp occur on this current jug and at the present moment all three can be found so there is no perceived difference in value. The variation is in the number of written lines. Some jugs have only the line "Hand made and hand decorated", other jugs have this line and the modelling credit to Robert Tabennor. The third has both lines plus the design credit to Jerry D. Griffith.

Okoboji Indian Reservation
North American Indian

A special commission in 1973 for a reunion dinner for the organisation which took place in Texas. Current value £300/$700.

Issued in 1973
current value
£400-£600/$1000-$1400

Bottle Oven

"Fired in the last firing of a Traditional Bottle Oven 1978". Incorporated onto a few jugs only. Highly valuable.

Special Commissions and Limited Editions

Royal Doulton in the 1980s released a variety of special and limited edition character jugs. Some of these have been for special promotional events such as new shop openings, while others have been external commissions from companies or organisations. These commissions have varied from colourways to wholly new characters. The edition size has varied from 1000 to 9500. The past four years has seen an enormous growth in these commissions. Some commissions have increased in value once sold out. A few of these increases have been quite staggering. The Higbee Mad Hatter, for example, released in 1985 in a limited edition of 250 priced at $250 has touched $1000, although it has now settled around the $500 mark. The market for these releases had reached its peak by 1989 with several of that year's releases failing to sell out. This has been reflected in the reduced edition size of recent introductions and a fall in special commissions. Apart, that is, from Royal Doulton's own Lawleys by Post which continues to flourish in producing large editions of small size character jugs. Listed below are details of all the special commissions released since 1978 and their issue price and current value if now sold out.

INTRO-DUCED	NAME	QUANTITY	TYPE	FOR	ISSUE PRICE	CURRENT VALUE
1978	JOHN BARLEYCORN	7500	RE-ISSUE	ROYAL DOULTON	$80	£120
1981	JOHN DOULTON		NEW JUG	RDICC		
1983	GRANT & LEE	9500	NEW JUG	ROYAL DOULTON	£45	£120
1984	CUSTER & SITTNG BULL	9500	NEW JUG	ROYAL DOULTON	£49	£75
1984	RONALD REAGAN	5000/ 2000	NEW JUG	REPUBLICAN COMMITTEE	£234	£270
1984	SIR HENRY DOULTON		NEW JUG	RDICC		
1985	ANTONY & CLEOPATRA	9500	NEW JUG	ROYAL DOULTON	£55	£65
1985	MR QUAKER	3500	NEW JUG	QUAKER OATS	£34	£225
1985	MAD HATTER	250	COLOURWAY	HIGBEE	$250	$600
1985	SANTA ANNA & DAVY CROCKETT	7500	NEW JUG	ROYAL DOULTON	£55	£60
1986	CRICKETER	500	NEW JUG	HAMPSHIRE C/CLUB	£25	£50
1986	OLD CHARLEY	250	COLOURWAY	HIGBEE	$250	$600
1986	SAIREY GAMP	250	COLOURWAY	STRAWBRIDGE & CLOTHIER	$250	$600
1986	WILLIAM GRANT	500	NEW JUG	GRANTS WHISKY	£120	£320

Year	Name	Qty	Type	Retailer	Price 1	Price 2
1987	WILLIAM GRANT	2500	NEW JUG	GRANTS WHISKY	£120	£200
1987	GOLFER	1000	COLOURWAY	JOHN SINCLAIR	£32	£45
1987	N AMERICAN INDIAN	1000	COLOURWAY	JOHN SINCLAIR	£32	£45
1987	RIP VAN WINKLE	1000	COLOURWAY	JOHN SINCLAIR	£32	£45
1987	SCARAMOUCHE	1500	COLOURWAY	CHINA GUILD	£34	£75
1987	QUEEN VICTORIA	3000	COLOURWAY	CHINA GUILD	£34	£70
1987	FALSTAFF	1500	COLOURWAY	UK FAIRS	£45	£55
1987	JOHN LENNON	1000	COLOURWAY	JOHN SINCLAIR	£25	£95
1987	SAIREY GAMP (sm)	250	COLOURWAY	STRAWBRIDGE & CLOTHIER	$125	£100
1987	OLD CHARLEY (sm)	250	COLOURWAY	HIGBEE	$125	£100
1987	MAD HATTER	250	COLOURWAY	HIGBEE	$125	£100
1987	THE SLEUTH	5000	COLOURWAY	LAWLEYS	£20	
1987	FALCONER	1000	COLOURWAY	PETER JONES	£33	
1987	LONG SILVER SILVER	250	COLOURWAY	D. H. HOLMES	$250	
1987	FALCONER	250	COLOURWAY	HORNES	$250	
1987	JOHN BARLEYCORN	625	NEW JUG	AMERICAN EXPRESS	$80	$400
1987	CANDY CANE SANTA	1000	NEW HANDLE	ROYAL DOULTON	$80	$1000/ £450
1987	HOLLY SANTA	7000	NEW HANDLE	ROYAL DOULTON	$80	$300/ £150
1988	SIR FRANCIS DRAKE	6000	NEW JUG	RETAIL GUILD	£45	
1988	THE POSTMAN	5000	NEW JUG	LAWLEYS	£25	
1988	THE COLLECTOR	5000	NEW JUG	KEVIN FRANCIS	£69	£90
1988	ANTIQUE DEALER	5000	NEW JUG	KEVIN FRANCIS	£63	£80
1988	THE AUCTIONEER	5000	NEW JUG	KEVIN FRANCIS	£63	£80
1988	PENDLE WITCH	5000	NEW JUG	KEVIN FRANCIS	£55	£90
1988	ENGINE DRIVER	5000	NEW JUG	LAWLEYS US RETAILERS	£25	
1988	CHELSEA PENSIONER	250	BACKSTAMP	5 RETAIL EDITIONS		
1988	YACHTSMAN	750	BACKSTAMP	SITE OF THE GREEN		
1988	GRANT	5000	NEW HANDLE	GRANTS WHISKY	£125	£200
1988	QUEEN VICTORIA	3000	COLOURWAY & BACKSTAMP	RETAIL GUILD	£41	
1988	ARAMIS	1000	COLOURWAY	P JONES	£42.50	
1988	ATHOS	1000	COLOURWAY	P JONES	£42.50	
1988	PORTHOS	1000	COLOURWAY	P JONES	£42.50	

1988	JOHN LENNON	1000	COLOURWAY	JOHN SINCLAIR	£25	£90
1988	LITTLE MESTER	3500	COLOURWAY	JOHN SINCLAIR	£65	
1988	PHILIP OF SPAIN	9500	NEW JUG	LAWLEYS	£25	
1988	ELIZABETH I	9500	NEW JUG	LAWLEYS	£25	
1988	KING ARTHUR & GUINEVERE	9500	NEW JUG	ROYAL DOULTON	£65	£70
1988	SAMSON & DELIAH	9500	NEW JUG	ROYAL DOULTON	£55	
1988	MICHAEL DOULTON	9500	NEW JUG	MD EVENTS	£25	
1988	BEEFEATER (Tiny)		NEW JUG	RDICC	£14	£25
1989	DICK WHITTINGTON	5000	NEW JUG	RETAIL GUILD	£65	
1989	FIREMAN	5000	NEW JUG	LAWLEYS	£27.50	
1989	POLICEMAN	5000	NEW JUG	LAWLEYS	£29.50	
1989	DUKE OF WELLINGTON	5000	NEW JUG	UKI CERAMICS	£75	
1989	SANTA	1000	COLOURWAY	AMERICAN COLLECTORS GUILD	£110	
1989	W. G. GRACE	9500	NEW JUG	LAWLEYS	£39	
1989	LEPRECHAUN	750	BACKSTAMP	SITE OF THE GREEN	$100	
1990	WASHINGTON	ANNUAL	BACKSTAMP	DOULTON	£45	
1990	RING MASTER	750	BACKSTAMP	LAMBETH PRODUCTIONS	£115	
1990	OLD KING COLE (Tiny)		NEW SIZE	RDICC	£14	£25
1990	ELEPHANT TRAINER	750	BACKSTAMP	HIGBEE		
1990	CHURCHILL	9500	NEW JUG	LAWLEYS	£45	
1990	MOUNTBATTEN	9500	NEW JUG	LAWLEYS	£45	
1990	MONTGOMERY	9500	NEW JUG	LAWLEYS	£45	
1990	GUY FAWKES	750	BACKSTAMP	CANADA	$195	
1990	YEOMAN OF THE GUARD		BACKSTAMP	4 RETAIL EDITIONS		
1991	GENERAL GORDON	1500	NEW JUG	UKI CERAMICS	£120	
1991	SMALL COLLECTOR	1500	SMALL SIZE	KEVIN FRANCIS	£49.95/$125	
1991	JOHN SHORTER	1500	NEW JUG	AUS C&TJ SOC	$125	
1991	BASEBALL PLAYER	500	BACKSTAMP	FLORIDA DOULTON FAIR	$110	
1991	HENRY VIII	1991	NEW JUG	DOULTON	£150	£250
1991	SOLDIER/SAILOR/ AIRMAN	250	THREE COLOURWAYS	BRITISH TOBY	$465 per set	

1991	CHARLES DICKENS (Small)	7500	NEW JUG	RDICC	£35
1991	FORTUNE TELLER	ANNUAL	NEW JUG	DOULTON	£55
1991	HEROES OF THE BLITZ	9500	THREE JUGS	LAWLEYS	£119 per set
1991	SMALL QUEEN VICTORIA	1500	SMALL SIZE	PASCOE & CO	£39/$95
1991	THE JESTER	2500	NEW TOBY JUG	DOULTON	£49.95
1991	CHRISTOPHER COLUMBUS (Small)	7500	BACKSTAMP	RDICC	£35
1991	SNAKE CHARMER	2500	NEW JUG USA ONLY	HIGBEE PRE-RELEASE	£120
1991	LEPRECHAUN (Small)	500	BACKSTAMP	SITE OF THE GREEN	
1991	SANTA CLAUS (Mini)		LIMITED BY TIME	US RETAILERS & RDICC	£20
1992	BILL SHANKLEY	5500	NEW JUG	LIVERPOOL FC	
1992	BAHAMAS POLICEMAN	1000	NEW JUG	ISLAND GIFTS	£120
1992	GENERAL EISENHOWER	1000	NEW JUG	UKI CERAMICS	£120
1992	WINSTON CHURCHILL	ANNUAL	NEW JUG	DOULTON	£75

Large and Small size Collector

Colour Variations

As interest has grown in collecting character jugs colour variations of the same model have become evident. Some of these have been quite significant whilst others have been relatively minor. Some variations seem to depend on the whims of the Doulton paintresses as in the case of the order for the black and white stripes on the hat of the Falconer. The reasons behind such changes are many and varied.

In some cases there is an official colour change sanctioned by Doulton, such as the colour of 'Arry's hair in 1951. On others there has been a slight change to the colour mix used like that on the Gardener's hat which has gone from brown to grey.

Other changes are more interesting, like the Red Hat Mad Hatter which was reportedly re-designed in the 1960s by a painter in the factory. Little did he know then that collecting fever would eventually make this 'one off' very valuable. This can be seen by the Henry V that I have coined a 'yellow crown'. These are seconds which have significant colour changes. In this case the red and gold colouring on the hat and flag has been omitted. The end result is a significant colour variation.

In many cases a colour change can make a great difference to the value of a jug. A good example of this is the Yellow Crown Old King Cole which is worth at least 15 times the value of the normal jug. Another example is the Blue Pearly Boy which is a variation of the brown.

Antique Dealer Colour Trials

Other interesting but less valuable changes have occurred with several jugs such as the eyes of Chief Sitting Bull of the Antagonist Series available with grey or blue eyes.

In most cases the change in colouring or absence of painting on parts of the jug are due to cost cutting by Royal Doulton. An area where this has particularly occurred is in hair colour changes during the 1950s. Jugs like the Cardinal can be found with grey, brown or white hair as a result of this, and many jugs, such as Bacchus, have undergone slight colouring changes on their handles, in this case the leaves are white and on others they are green. These tiny modifications of colouring evolve slowly through the production life of a character jug.

In other cases if the colour is quite significantly different it is likely to have been produced as a painter's private piece or as part of a pilot batch. An example of the former is the Red Hat Mad Hatter which is said to be a painter's private piece. In cases like this the value of the piece is solely the preserve of the person buying it. As these pieces are by their nature unique the sky is the limit. The prices likely to be reached at the top end of the American collector market can be well into five figures. As all jugs are initially piloted one can expect a few more 'experimental pieces' to appear on the market. In recent years Royal Doulton has increased security in the factory to prevent pilot pieces disappearing. In the past it was considered to be a perk of the job to take them, so there is every likelihood that more will appear.

Nightwatchman

Captain Ahab

Colour Fakes

As the value of colour variations seems to have 'gone through the roof' there has been considerable speculation that some unscrupulous people would start colouring up white jugs. A collector buying a colour variation should check the base of the jug around the rim for any black marks or line which would indicate that the jug has been refired. All white jugs that have been sold were glazed, so refiring would cause a moisture burn on the base of the jug. A further check is whether the jug itself is perfect; 99% of white jugs have some form of damage. A final check is the quality of finish; fake colours are likely to be weak and not have the Doulton gloss to them.

Valuing Collections

This booklet will only give the approximate replacement value of a collection, not its selling value, which could be considerably lower. The only way to sell a collection at its replacement value is to sell it to another collector prepared to pay the market price. If this is not possible, the only alternatives are to sell the whole collection to a Doulton Character Jug dealer, or through an auctioneer. A reputable dealer will pay 15% to 30% below the price which he/she feels that they can obtain by reselling the character jugs. The price offered will vary according to the size of the collection and the individual dealer.

The great advantage of selling to dealers is the speed at which hard cash can be raised from part, or all, of a collection. Alternatively, collections or individual jugs can be sold through auction. In this case there is no guarantee as to the exact price the jug will reach and the auctioneer's commission, usually about 15%, will be deducted from the amount raised. Goods are required to be entered for auction some weeks before the auction date and cheques will not be issued until one or two weeks after the sale takes place. A minimum price can be set for each jug which ensures that it will not be sold below this price, but a percentage of this price will usually be charged if the owner is unable to sell. However, as previously stated, auctions can produce a price that is well above the open market price.

Part of the Tom Power collection

Rarities

As the title suggests the purpose of this section is to illustrate a group of character jugs which are so rare that market value outstrips all other discontinued character jugs. In most cases these jugs are what is known as 'pilot jugs'. They are prototypes of jugs that did not go into production and somehow escaped onto the market. Other rarities are mould variations on characters subsequently produced over a number of years or jugs produced in very limited numbers for one reason or another. Market values when possible are given, but many of these jugs are so rare they rarely if ever appear on the market and subsequently are impossible to value. Other rarities are to be found in the colour variations section.

Red, White and Brown Hair Clowns

Excepting the brown variation, red and white hair clowns are neither pilots nor colour variations but are two character jugs which have undergone a full production run. Their high market values, however, mean they must be classified as rarities even though both are fairly easily obtained on the discontinued market.

Red Hair Clown — Large — Produced 1937-42
Market Value £750-£850 $2000-$2700
White Hair Clown — Large — Produced 1951-55
Market Value £400-£500 $1000-$1200
Brown Hair Clown
This jug is a variation of the red hair clown first discovered in 1985. Bearing the same registration number as the red hair version D5610 it has brown coloured hair and slightly different facial markings and colourings. Its value is judged to be equal to that of the red hair clown.

The Black Hair Clown

This is an ordinary red hair clown that was produced with black hair by special commission in the 1930s for a Lancashire clown renowned for his jet black hair. Only one version known to exist.

The Falstaff Prototype

An early trial example of the Falstaff dating from 1943, the jug was only introduced in 1950 and still current. This prototype has significant colouring differences.

Market Value   Very difficult to determine

The Falstaff prototype

Miniature Old Salt

The character 'Old Salt' was introduced as a large and small size character jug in 1961 and is still produced today. In 1983 it was introduced in the miniature size with a small handle change, there is no longer a space in the crook of the mermaid's arm. At least 100 exist with the original handle, presumably pilots made before the design changed. These jugs after a slightly strange start are now established in value.

Market Value: £250-£350 $700-$1000

Miniature Old Salt and prototype

Single Rat Pied Piper Handle

This is the prototype for the Pied Piper jug produced between 1954 and 1980. The significant difference, apart from the colouring, is the one large white rat across the top of the handle instead of the 3 small brown rats on the usual models. It was felt that it looked too much like a white mouse but it was painted and fired in 1958 by its designer, Geoff Blower, four years after the substitute went into general production. When it sold in 1986 it brought £7000 through private sale. Today's value is much higher.

The normal Pied Piper left and Single Rat version right

Small & Miniature Yachtsman

These pilots are now confirmed as existing. An example of both turned up in the Midlands in 1984 and reportedly sold for over £1000 each. None have been reported since and one would therefore expect the market value to now be around £1400-£1600/$2000-$2500.

The Scarlet Pimpernel

This jug was submitted by designer Geoff Blower in the 1950s in the form of a clay model. It was subsequently rejected by a marketing committee in Royal Doulton and supposedly destroyed. There must however have been a mould made as an example was discovered in the Stoke-on-Trent area in 1987. The jug was reportedly sold for in excess of £15000 to an American dealer and it now occupies pride of place in an American collection. Despite the questions surrounding the jug it is unquestionably from the 1950s original clay model and is considered unique. Picture — colour section.

Goatee Beard Cavalier

This is another early version which went through a mould change, although in this case it was only minor. This version has a distinctive goatee beard as opposed to the bare chin of later models. In recent years very few examples of this jug have appeared on the market. The conclusion that this is a very rare jug is upheld by its high market price. Originally thought to have only been made in the large size, a small size has now been reported to exist. I have not seen this jug so cannot confirm its existence. It would of course be highly valuable.

Large: £1400-£1800 $3000-$4000

The Goatee Beard Cavalier (right)

Toothless Granny

Not considered to be as rare as other mould variations, this jug is identifiable by its lack of a prominent front tooth. It is reported to almost always carry an 'A' mark. There are other slight variations with the normal Granny, particularly in their hairlines. The market value of this jug has suffered in recent years having touched £800 in the past. Such high prices resulted in many more being 'discovered' by the non-collecting public. Recorded as only being produced in the large size there are persistent rumours of it existing in a small size. It is my opinion that it does not exist in the small size and I suspect that slight differences in painting are responsible for such rumours.

Market Value: £350-£450 $800-$1000

The Toothless Granny (right)

Yellow Crown Old King Cole 1938-39

An early version of the Old King Cole has a yellow crown as opposed to the more common orange. It also has other variations as both versions were made from completely different moulds. The 'yellow crown' was made in both large and small sizes, the small size being the rarer of the two. The jug is known to exist without mould variations in both sizes. Due to its rarity the market values given are tentative.

Large:	£2200-£2800	$6000-$7000
Small:	£1700-£2000	$8000-$12000
Large Musical	£1800-£2000	$8000-$10000
Ordinary Musical	£1000-£1500	$4000-$5000

The Yellow Crown Old King Cole (left)

Pierre Trudeau

Royal Doulton sought approval to do this jug whilst Trudeau was still the Prime Minister of Canada. Unfortunately, by the time they had finished the prototype almost three years later, he had been defeated, re-elected and finally retired. It was a fine looking jug with an elaborate Canadian flag handle with his trademark red rose in the handle. Two trials were produced, one with on glaze red, the second with under glaze red. Picture — Colour Section.

Antony and Cleopatra Prototype

Recently surfacing onto the market this must be an early prototype. If one looks closely there are very slight modelling and painting changes on this jug as compared to the production model. The change is particularly noticeable on the Roman nose of Antony. The value of this jug is again difficult to determine and must be left to the pocket book of the eventual buyer. It is our opinion that he will have to dig deep! Picture — Colour Section.

Clark Gable, Hatless Drake and Groucho Marx

Clark Gable

This jug was initially produced for the current Celebrity series in 1984. For some reason the first shipment of these jugs to the USA was recalled, however at least 250 of these jugs had been sold to the public. All the jugs recalled were subsequently destroyed and plans to produce the model were dropped. This was due to Clark Gable's estate not approving the likeness. The jug has subsequently shot up in value, as there is no doubt that the jug now holds a pilot rarity rating.

Market Value: £1500-£2000 $3000-$4000

Hatless Drake

The existence of this jug was only confirmed in 1981, yet since then a surprising number have appeared. At least six were available at one of the 1984 specialist Doulton fairs. Originally thought to be another mould variation, it must have in fact been an early version of the Drake character jug. It only exists in the large size and a colour variation with a green instead of red jacket is known, which sells for a premium price.

Market Value: £1300-£1700 $4000-$5000

Groucho Marx

This character jug was in production between 1984 and 1987 as part of the Celebrity series. A prototype was originally produced with two of Groucho's brothers peering around the cigar. It would seem that high production costs led to the removal of the brothers from the production-run version. Only one example of the handle prototype is known to exist in a USA collection and its value would be easily into five figures. Picture — Colour Section.

Grant and Lee Bone China Prototype

This example found in 1986 must be some form of initial trial for the very successful Grant and Lee limited edition. Made in bone china it is slightly smaller than the original with different flag markings and gold instead of yellow on the braid trim. Picture — Colour Section.

The Horn Handle John Peel *The Red Gardener*

Horn Handle John Peel

This unusual modelling variation is considered unique and is currently in the hands of family in Canada. The jug was a parting gift from colleagues to an ex-employee of Doulton who was emigrating to Canada. The base of the jug is inscribed "Good Hunting Jacko". It is not known if the piece was a pilot or just a personal one off so there may well be others in existence. To date none have appeared. Despite reports to contrary its authenticity is beyond doubt.

The 'Red' Gardener

A trial colouring for the Gardener. The main difference being a striped shirt and red neckerchief with a far darker brown hat. This example would have been produced in 1972/73.

Market Valuation: Very difficult to determine

Macbeth Handle Prototype

This character jug was first introduced in 1982. The jug featured here is an early trial example with a different handle to the one eventually put into production. This handle prototype found its way onto the market in 1988. The actual market value is very difficult to determine but it would almost certainly, on today's market, bring well over £2000. Picture — Colour Section.

Romeo Handle Prototype

The story behind this character is exactly the same as the previously mentioned Macbeth. This example was reportedly found at the same time. The handle variation in this case is far more extensive and was presumably altered for cost purposes. Its value would be on a par with the The Macbeth. Picture — Colour Section. See additional listings for other versions.

From left to right: Higbee Mad Hatter, ordinary bone china Mad Hatter and the "Red Hat" Mad Hatter

Red Hat Mad Hatter

Only discovered this year the jug dates from the 1960s. The story behind it is; a painter in the factory wanted a Mad Hatter but did not like the original colours. He accordingly redesigned the colour and had it painted up in the factory. When finally sold in the USA the jug brought over $10000.

The Yellow Crown Henry V

This is a factory second which is missing the gold and red colours. Instead the yellow base colour is prominent creating a very different effect. When found and sold in 1986 the 1982 production brought a significant price due to its uniqueness. Since then at least 40 have been found and its value has dropped. Current value: £400/$1200.

The Yellow Crown Henry V (right) and the normal version

The Miniature Trapper and Lumberjack

The Pilot Baseball Player

The half size Jockey alongside the normal

Miniature Trapper

A surprising number of pilot versions have turned up in the past four years, particularly in the UK. There must have been several sample pieces produced before the character was withdrawn in all sizes.

Market Value: £800-£1200 $1800-$2400

Miniature Lumberjack

Produced and withdrawn in the same year as the Trapper jugs. The Lumberjack jugs also have miniature pilot versions occasionally turning up. Their existence and story is identical to that of the miniature Trapper and it is judged to be of comparable value.

Market Value: £800-£1200 $1800-$2400

Half Size Jockey

Two versions of this are reported to exist, both of which, although not carrying the Doulton backstamp, have been confirmed as Doulton's by the International Collectors Club. The example photographed in this book is in the hands of a private collector in Sheffield.

The Baseball Player

This is a pilot produced in the early 1970s and never put into production. The designer was David Biggs and two colourways exist, one in red and the other in blue. The jugs are held in private collections and it is highly unlikely that one will appear on the open market. If an example were to appear it would probably bring in excess of £20000/$35000.

The Maori

This is a pilot jug produced in 1938 and 1939 in large size. Two different versions were made and at least six examples of the jug illustrated are known. It seems that some were actually sold through retail outlets, so there may well be others waiting to be found. One example owned by a purchaser of the second edition of this book sold it for £12000 in 1986. The value of any example now would be considerably higher.

Buffalo Bill

Another pilot jug that was never put into full production. Only three examples are known. If an example were to appear it would probably bring in excess of £20000/$35000.

Buffalo Bill   *The Maori*

Union Jack Handle Guardsman

As can be seen by the photograph the original handle was a full bodied Union Jack. Two colour patterns were attempted, both were considered too complicated to paint and too awkward for decals — hence the simpler damask the jug eventually received.

The Williamsburg Pilots

These three variations were found in 1985 in the Midlands and subsequently sold for a few hundred pounds. These are the only versions known and are significant pilot pieces, varying in both modelling and painting. Their current market value is difficult to determine.

The Williamsburg Pilots

The Granny Lighter

According to the records only 12 small size character jugs were adopted as lighters and the Granny was not amongst them. In 1989, a granny lighter turned up which apparently is a pilot produced in the 1950s. The value of this jug is not as high as other pilots as it is not the true sense of the word a pilot jug but rather a pilot miscellaneous item.

The Granny Lighter

Coloured Winston Churchill

White Churchill

Not really a character jug, although regarded as one by collectors. It is a loving cup with two handles, produced between 1940-41. This extremely rare jug has an inscription on its base which reads "Winston Spencer Churchill Prime Minister 1940. This loving cup was made during the 'Battle of Britain' as a tribute to a great leader". Coloured versions of this jug are known to exist. one of which is restored. These coloured jugs do not carry an inscription. Differing slightly in colouring shades, they have blue shoulders and bow ties with coloured hair and pale complexion. In 1989 Sotheby's Chester sold a coloured variation for £16500.

White Churchill: £3500-£4500 $7000-$9000

McCallum

A large size jug made in the mid-thirties to early forties for D.M. McCallum Whisky Distillers. It depicts a typical Highlander Scot and three variations are known to exist. Other manufacturers of the period, particularly Wade, produced identical jugs excepting the backstamp which are of small value compared to Doulton versions.

Kingsware McCallum
Produced in the distinctive brown Kingsware glaze this jug is highly sought after by collectors. A very rare jug which is highly valued on the Doulton markets. Between 1000 and 1500 are known to have been produced.

Market Value: £1250-£1500 $2500-$3500

The White McCallum
Identical to the Kingsware version except for its lack of colouring and different glazing, this jug is the more common of the two. It is nearly always crazed on the outside.

Market Value: £700-£800 $1100-$1400

The Coloured McCallum
A pilot variation whose value is impossible to determine and authenticity is under question.

The Pearly Girl

A very rare white Pearly Boy

A large 'Arry with a small blue Pearly Boy, a miniature brown and white Pearly Boy and the tiny 'Arry

The Pearly Boy and Pearly Girl (Limited production brown 1946—1952 and blue 1946)

These are a variation of the 'Arry and 'Arriet and represent the traditional cockney Pearly Kings and Queens. The Pearly Boy is identifiable by the 'pearls' or 'buttons' running down his head, side of jug and around the collar. There are several colour variations amongst the pearly boys and all are considered very rare. The three versions are brown, brown and white, and blue; blue being the rarest. One further version is known with a beige hat, brown coat and white buttons, two examples of this jug have been reported.

Pearly Boy:	Brown		Blue	
Large:	£600-£800	$1200-$1400	£4500-£6000	$8000-$9000
Small:	£150-£175	$400-$500	£1500-£2000	$4000-$4500
Miniature:	£100-£150	$500-$600	Not known	

Pearly girls have no additional buttons and except for the colouring are identical to the 'Arriet jug. It has a bright lime green handle and hat feather. The hat brim is red/maroon, as is the large button at base of the feather. The hair is very dark brown, and the scarf is bright red. The pearly girls are far rarer than the pearly boys, and although particularly valuable it is difficult to put an exact value on them. A colour variation of the large size has been found in Canada. This has a dark brown coat as compared to the normal dark blue colouring.

Yellow Handle Beefeater

On this Beefeater the lettering on the back of the jug along with the crown is coloured yellow. This took place on early GR versions only and exists in both a large and small size. See handle variations section. Picture — Colour Section.

Market Value
Large £800-£1000 $2000-$2500
Small £700-£950 $1000-$1200

George Washington

This is the original Washington jug in a part-painted form. This exceptionally large jug (approx 1½ inches bigger than normal) played a part in its rejection, as the decorating staff are almost entirely women and they literally could not carry a whole shelf loaded with the jugs. None of these prototypes are known to have reached the market.

Celebrity Prototypes

The jugs featured in the photograph are members of the Celebrity series which ran into legal problems with the launch of the Clark Gable jug. Marilyn Monroe and Humphrey Bogart have managed to find their way out of the factory. No sight of an Elvis Presley yet! Picture — Colour Section.

Silver Rim Parson Brown

This small size was bought by a collector five years ago. The silver rim is dated for 1937 when the jug was introduced. There is no record of the piece being produced with a silver rim although there are many other examples of a silver rim being applied to other types of Doulton ware. It was possibly added by a jeweller at the time, on the private instructions of a collector. Whilst the amount of silver present will not add much intrinsic value to the piece it would command a fair premium given its rarity value today.

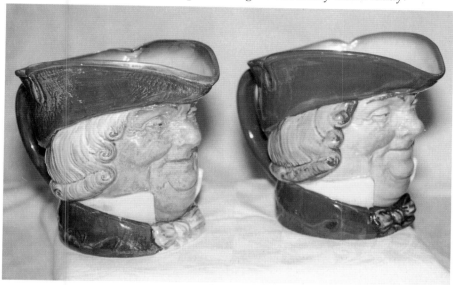

John Wesley Toby

Produced in Burslem in the 1920s the jug was modelled by Charles Noke who decided not to put it into production as it was thought slightly unsuitable for a religious person who abstained from drink to be cast as a Toby. There were only two examples made, one now resides in the museum of the Wesley church in Tasmania while the other was kept by Charles Noke's assistant and presumably is still kept by that family. Current market value would be around £15000 were one to appear. Picture — See Toby Jug Section

Terry Fox

A promotional/charity character jug along the lines of Toby Gillette. Terry Fox, who had lost a leg to cancer, attempted to run a marathon across Canada to raise money for fellow sufferers. The character jug was produced in an edition of three only with one being kept for the Doulton collection, one being kept by Mrs Fox and the final jug being auctioned for charity at the first Canadian Doulton Collectors fair in 1990. The auctioned jug went for Can$31000, approximately £15000.

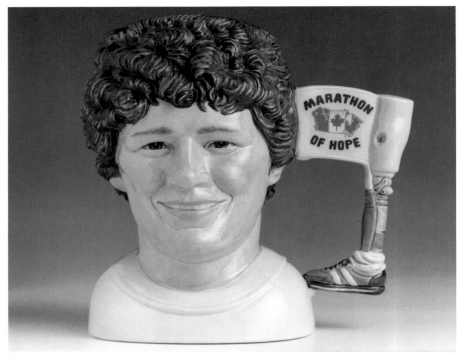

Terry Fox

Miniature Pearly Boy and Girl

These were never recorded as being produced but last year a couple of examples were bought by an American collector. The jugs look convincing with the delicate pearly colourings. Close examination however reveals a lack of modelling to the buttons. My conclusions are that these were either trial colourings done at the time to test the concept or the alternative scenario is that the buttons have been added later by a restorer to fake the piece. There seems to be no evidence of repainting and a lack of refiring marks, but in today's uncertain marketplace question marks will always exist over pieces such as this.

D'Artagnan

Another 1980s prototype that was rejected for release. It can be seen here in Eric Griffiths old office at Royal Doulton along with several other prototypes. This was at a time when no great worth was attached to these jugs and the storage arrangements were not particularly security conscious. The current whereabouts of the jug is unknown but it would certainly command a high price were it to be located.

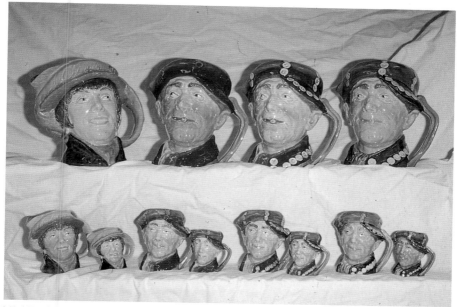

Mini Pearly Boy and Girl

D'Artagnan

Miller and Wife of Bath

These jugs, modelled by William Harper, were part of a proposed Canterbury Tales series. The idea was eventually rejected and the jugs now form part of the company's prototype display. Their value would be high if they were to escape on to the market.

Catherine of Aragon Prototype Handle

Two alternative handles produced as prototypes for marketing considerations in 1975 and rejected in favour of the Tower. Their value would be in excess of £2000/$5,000

Small Size Falstaff Colour Trial

This colour trial was painted to determine the viability of small size follow up to the large size Falstaff commission by UK Ceramics. The concept was dropped but one of the trials did escape into the marketplace and is now residing in an American collection.

Romeo Prototype Handles

Another jug which went though several modifications to the handle until Royal Doulton were satisfied. Of the two prototypes the handle with the figure would be worth the most, possibly around a couple of thousand pounds.

The Pilgrim Father

A prototype from the 1970s that never went into production. It is believed to have been modelled by David Biggs and it is likely that only one example was cast and painted. The prototype is in Royal Doulton's own collection and has been exhibited at the UK Doulton fairs. A very important and valuable prototype.

Uncle Tom Cobbleigh

Modelled in 1975 by Robert Tabbenor, this prototype never proceeded. As an exciting new discovery this jug would be valued very highly indeed on the market, possibly in excess of five figures.

Keys Handle Beefeater

Produced in 1988 as a possible commission for P W C Publishing the project was eventually abandoned. It would seem that the original prototype did not make it back to Royal Doulton as it is believed to be residing in a Canadian collection. Given its uncertain status, value is impossible to determine.

Toby Gillette

This jug was produced in 1984, in an edition of three, as result of a request made to a children's TV programme entitled Jim'll Fix It. A boy of 12 named Toby Gillette wrote to Jimmy Saville asking if he could have a toby jug made of himself. With the co-operation of Doulton, three character jugs were made and the whole process was featured in the TV programme. One of the three jugs was presented to Toby Gillette, one was kept for the Royal Doulton museum and the third was given to Jimmy Saville to auction for charity. This jug brought £14500 plus commission when auctioned at Sotheby's in 1986. Toby Gillette put his own jug up for sale though Sotheby's and this example brought £14000 plus commission.

Robin Hood

Modelled by Eric Griffiths in 1987, mid size prototype is really of a tankard than a traditional character jug. There is similarity in style between this jug and the Barleycorn jug produced for American Express. This is the only example known of the jug and it resides in an American collection. Current market value in excess of £5000/$10000.

The Scarlet Pimpernel

The Macbeth Prototype

John Gilpen

The Celebrity Prototypes

The Groucho Marx Prototype

Front and back of the Anthony and Cleopatra Prototype

Romeo Prototype

Pierre Trudeau Prototype

Mae West Prototype

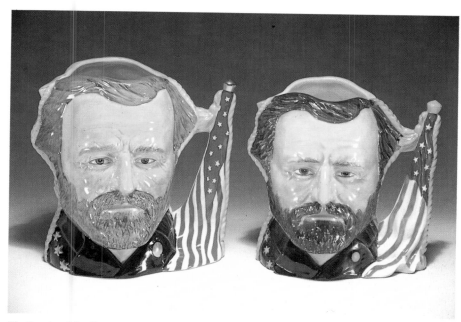

The Grant and Lee Prototype with standard version

Gold Handle Beefeater

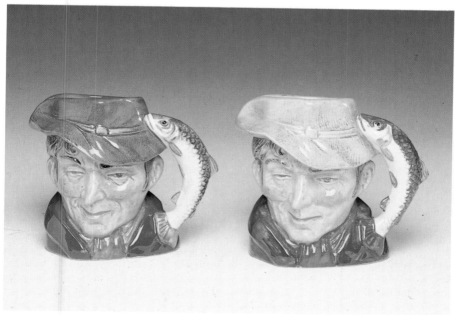

A small Poacher in varying colour shades

A small brown Pearly Boy with white buttons and a large Pearly Boy

Several colour shades of the Gardener

The Pendle Witch colour trials

The Collector, Antique Dealer and Auctioneer

The 1987 John Barleycorn and Holly Leaf Santa

A Sairey Gamp toothpick holder and sugar

Mr Toby. Author Vic Schuler with his special Kevin Francis Peggy Davies Toby Jug

The large size prototype character jug "Cabinet Maker" designed in 1963 but never put into production as series was withdrawn in 1983

Reverse of the "Cabinet Maker"

The large size prototype of the "Toothless Granny" circa 1935

The reverse of "Toothless Granny"

Investing in Royal Doulton Character Jugs

For the past ten years the value of discontinued character jugs has risen steadily and consequently collectors have benefited from their investment. While it is difficult to estimate the average growth in values which varies tremendously between individual jugs there is no doubt that anyone who has speculated in character jugs over the past ten years has enjoyed a rate of return on the value of his investment which is comparable to money invested in more traditional areas such as building societies or banks. However from a strictly business point of view I would not recommend people to invest in jugs. The potential returns are no longer particularly attractive on most jugs and the amount of work involved when buying further reduces the real rate of return. There are many other more secure forms of investment which could produce higher returns for considerably less effort and organisation.

From a collector's point of view, the investment aspect of collecting character jugs should be seen as a welcome bonus something to bear in mind whilst collecting. A return should never be seen as an end in itself and must always be viewed as secondary to the joys of collecting. The pleasure to be gained from acquiring a particular jug and displaying it in one's collection is worth far more to the true collector than any growth in its value.

The only secure way to make money from investing in jugs is to find a bargain. A Pearly Girl selling for £3 at a boot fair would give a guaranteed profit of £2997, whilst a colour variation on a current jug which has slipped through Doulton's quality control would net you several hundred pounds! There are still bargains to be found and the only way to give yourself a chance of finding one is to know your character jugs.

It is, however, sensible for collectors to benefit as much as possible from the investment potential of character jugs collected. For those who would appreciate advice on the subject there are a few relevant points listed below. It should be clear that these are general points of advice and that the author accepts no responsibility for action taken by the reader in light of his comments.

1   Try to buy at the lowest price possible. This is an obvious statement, but one which needs stressing as we are all prone to buying, "that expensive jug which I just had to have!" The secret is patience. Do not expect to complete any set in a short time, for in order to do it you will be forced to pay top money for certain jugs whilst a little more patience would have resulted in great savings.

2   Work hard at buying. Always try and shop around between dealers, shops and markets, and be prepared to travel to find those bargains. In this collecting area there is no doubt that hard work produces the results. For those who can take the strain, purchase at auction is recommended because prices can be considerably lower, the greater part of auction sales being made to trade purchasers.

3 Remember, the greater the investment made the greater the return. If values rise by 10% the jug that cost £700 will give you greater profit (£70) as compared to one that costs £100 (profit £10). This fact is slightly misleading for while being true it does tend to ignore the fact that the actual rate of return does not change and that by investing more you are not actually increasing the real rate of return. It could well be that the extra money spent to produce a greater profit in sum could in fact earn far more than 10% in another investment.

4 Rarity is always important, because prices are determined, not by dealers, or by price guides, but by market forces and the interaction of supply and demand. A limited supply will push prices upwards in spite of the normal level of demand. Therefore try to buy the rarer character jugs that were only in production for a few years and always pay close attention to those discontinuations announced by Royal Doulton every year.

5 It is also preferable to have the earliest version of any character jug as there are very real differences in the quality and detail of old and recent versions of the same jug.

6 Keep building up your knowledge of and contacts in the secondary market. The more information you have the more likely you are to spot the underpriced or very rare character jug. If you are aware of price trends, any jug which starts to move up in value is well worth buying because the chances are that it will continue to rise. Do not be afraid to ask questions and advice from dealers and other collectors, for while they may not be correct, everyone has an opinion that is worth hearing and it will help you build your own overall view of the market. The greater your contacts with dealers the more likely you are to obtain the character jug you require. All dealers have a favoured list of customers who benefit greatly from the dealer being fully aware of exactly what type of jug a collector requires and the price he is prepared to pay.

7 In the past two years several special commission Doulton character jugs have been released. Some have increased in value once sold out. The most desirable special commissions will be original editions as compared to colourways. The higher the quality the greater the future appreciation.

8 The collector needs to be careful when buying with investment in mind. A very good rule to follow is to only buy what you like. Remember if your investment is wrong you will have to live with it and it is those who are reluctant to sell who always get the best price.

Collecting Discontinued Character Jugs

For any new collector of character jugs, here is a list of buying tips to help you to build up your collection. Certain sections should also be of interest to existing collectors.

1   When buying from antique fairs or a market it is best to get there as early as possible because jugs that are rare or cheap are always sold early on, usually to the trade.

2   Be prepared to travel when searching for jugs as there are differences in both price and availability in different parts of the country. Try advertising locally you may be surprised by the results.

3   Shop around whenever possible as prices vary considerably between dealers even in the same antique fair or market.

4   Older jugs may have rust stains if they have been used as containers. Naval or petroleum jelly will remove these stains without marring the glaze.

5   Always examine jugs carefully under a strong light to detect hairline cracks or restoration. In addition to this ask a dealer to guarantee that the jug you are buying is perfect.

6   Get to know individual Doulton dealers. They will keep you in touch with developments in the Doulton market and could result in you obtaining pieces at favourable prices.

7   To obtain rarer jugs, try placing orders with individual dealers. A large proportion of pieces never appear on the open market but are sold directly to the collector who has previously placed an order with the dealer.

8   Contact auction houses in your area regularly to inquire if they have any jugs in forthcoming sales. It is relatively easy to leave bids if you can't attend the auction yourself.

9   Try to meet the collectors. This will be useful for buying or swapping jugs and you will derive even greater pleasure from making new friends as you do so.

10   The market value of discontinued jugs can rise or fall, so try to keep well informed. I suggest collectors note the prices they hear or see to ensure that they always buy in line with market prices.

11   Subscribe to the International Royal Doulton Collectors' Club. This organisation costs very little to join and provides several benefits to members who are issued with a three-monthly illustrated magazine with all the latest news on the Doulton world. For details and an

application form, contact any of the following branches:

UK Headquarters
Royal Doulton
Minton House
London Road
Stoke-on-Trent
ST4 7QD

USA Branch
Royal Doulton USA Inc
PO Box 1815
Somerset NJ 08873

Canadian Branch
Royal Doulton Canada Inc
850 Progress Avenue
Scarborough
Ontario MIH 3C4

Australian Branch
Royal Doulton Australia Pty Ltd
Inc NSW
PO Box 47
17-23 Merriwa Street
Gordon
NSW 2072

New Zealand
PO Box 2059
Auckland
New Zealand

12 Recommended UK Antique Fairs

All antique fairs are worth visiting as many antique dealers carry Doulton items. Those listed below are regularly attended by the author and usually have a few Doulton Specialist dealers displaying Doulton jugs.

See Exchange and Mart for details
Queens Hall Leeds
Bingly Hall Stafford
Birmingham
Alexandra Palace London
Doncaster Racecourse Yorkshire
Newark Showground Nottinghamshire

13 Recommended Antique Markets

Portobello Road, London
Notting Hill Gate is the nearest Tube station to the market which is held every Saturday.

Camden Passage, London.
Tube: Angel. Every Wednesday and Saturday. Home to two large specialised dealers with many others carrying Doulton as part of their general stock.

Alfies, Church Street, London.
Tube: Edgware Road. The London centre for Doulton dealing. There are two major Doulton dealers in Alfies and numerous other dealers who always have pieces of Doulton for sale.

14   **The Doulton Fairs**
The UK now has two Doulton Fairs held every year at the Park Lane Hotel in London in October and at the Stafford County showground in June. For further details and timing contact the Doulton Collectors Club. The USA has several Doulton fairs. For further information contact any American Dealer listed in the advertising section.

15   **UK Auctioneers**
All auction houses commonly sell Doulton along with other collection and antiques. The auction houses listed below all either hold special Doulton sales or regularly feature Doulton in general sales.

Phillips
7 Blenheim Street
London W1
Tel: 071 629 6602

Christies South Kensington
85 Old Brompton Road
London SW5 3JS
Tel: 071 581 7611

Louis Taylors
Percy Street
Hanley
Stoke-on-Trent
Tel: 0782 260222

Bonhams
Monpelier Street
Knightsbridge
London SW7 1HH
Tel: 071 584 9161

16   **Selected UK Current Doulton Retailers**
London — Kevin Francis Ceramics, 85 Landcroft Road, SE22
Tel: 081 693 1841
Manchester — T Hayward & Sons, 62/66 Deansgate
Glasgow — Trenons, 254 Sauchieshall Street
Edinburgh — Les Cadeaux, 121 Rose Street
York — Mulberry Hall, Stonegate
Swansea — David Evans, Princess Way
Sheffield — John Sinclair, Glossop Road

17   Subscribe to the independent magazine *Collecting Doulton*. Available from HP Publishing, 2 Strafford Avenue, Elsecar, Barnsley, South Yorkshire S74 8AA.

Alphabetical Listing of In-Production Character Jugs

Character	Year of Introduction	Large	Small	Medium
Airman	1991	●	◆	●
Angler	1991	●	◆	●
Beefeater	1983	◆	◆	●
Bonnie Prince Charlie	1990	◆	●	●
Bowls Player	1991	●	◆	●
Churchill (3rd Version)	1992	◆	●	●
Clown (2nd Version)	1990	◆	●	●
Columbus	1991	◆	●	●
D'Artagnan	1983	◆	●	●
Elephant Trainer	1990	◆	●	●
Falconer	1960	◆	◆	●
Falstaff	1950	◆	◆	●
Gardener (2nd Version)	1990	●	◆	●
George Washington	1982	◆	●	●
Golfer (1st Version)	1971	◆	●	●
Golfer (2nd Version)	1990	●	◆	●
Guardsman	1986	◆	●	●
Guy Fawkes	1990	◆	●	●
Henry VIII (1st Version)	1975	◆	◆	●
Henry VIII (2nd Version)	1991	◆	●	●
Jockey (2nd Version)	1991	●	◆	●
Lawyer	1959	◆	◆	●
Leprechaun	1990	◆	●	●
London Bobby	1986	◆	●	●
Long John Silver	1952	◆	◆	●
The Master	1991	●	◆	●
Merlin	1960	◆	◆	●
Montgomery of Alamein (3rd Version)	1992	◆	●	●
Old Salt	1961	◆	◆	●
Poacher	1955	◆	◆	●
Ring Master	1991	◆	●	●
Rip Van Winkle	1955	◆	◆	●
Robin Hood (2nd version)	1960	◆	◆	●
Sailor	1991	●	◆	●
Santa Claus (2nd Version)	1984	◆	◆	●

Sleuth	1973		◆	◆	●
Snooker Player	1991		●	◆	●
Soldier	1991		●	●	●
The Town Cryer (2nd Version)	1991		◆	●	●
Wizard	1990		◆	●	●
Yeoman of the Guard	1991		◆	●	●

◆ Sizes available   ● sizes not available

NB:At the end of 1991, Royal Doulton announced the withdrawal of all miniature size jugs from their range.

The Policeman

Alphabetical Listing of Discontinued Character Jugs

Character	Production Dates	Large	Small	Available in Miniature	Tiny	Intermediate
Anne Boleyn	1975-90	◆	◆	◆	●	◆
Anne of Cleves	1980-90	◆	◆	◆	●	●
Annie Oakley	1985	●	●	●	◆	●
Antony and Cleopatra	1985	◆	●	●	●	●
Apothecary	1963-83	◆	◆	◆	●	●
Aramis	1956-91	◆	◆	◆	●	●
'Ard of Earing	1964-67	◆	◆	◆	●	●
'Arriet	1947-60	◆	◆	◆	◆	●
'Arry	1956-91	◆	◆	◆	●	●
Athos	1938-86	◆	◆	◆	◆	●
Auld/Owd Mac	1959-91	◆	◆	◆	●	●
Bacchus		◆	◆	◆	●	●
Baseball Player	1991	●	◆	●	●	●
Beefeater (GR Handle)	1947-53	◆	◆	◆	●	●
Benjamin Franklin	1983-90	●	◆	●	●	●
Bootmaker	1963-83	◆	◆	◆	●	●
Blacksmith	1963-83	◆	◆	◆	●	●
Buffalo Bill	1985-90	●	●	●	●	◆
Busker	1988-91	◆	●	●	●	●
Buz Fuz	1948-60	●	◆	●	●	◆
Captain Ahab	1959-84	◆	◆	◆	●	●
Captain Cuttle	1948-60	●	◆	●	●	◆
Captain Henry Morgan	1958-81	◆	◆	◆	●	●
Captain Hook	1965-71	◆	◆	◆	●	●
Cardinal	1936-60	◆	◆	◆	◆	●
Catherine of Aragon	1975-90	◆	◆	◆	●	●
Catherine Howard	1978-90	◆	◆	◆	●	●
Catherine Parr	1981-90	◆	●	●	●	●
Cavalier	1940-60	◆	◆	●	●	●
Cavalier (goatee beard version)	1940	◆	●	●	●	●
Chelsea Pensioner	1989-91	◆	●	●	●	●
Churchill (1st version)	1940-42	◆	●	●	●	◆
City Gent	1988-91	◆	●	●	●	●
Clark Cable	1984					
Clown Red Hair	1937-42	◆	●	●	●	●
Clown White Hair	1951-55	◆	●	●	●	●
Clown Brown Hair	1937-42					
Cook and Cheshire Cat	1990-91	◆	●	●	●	●
Custer & Sitting Bull	1984	◆	●	●	●	●
Dick Turpin (1st version)	1935-60	◆	◆	◆	●	●
Dick Turpin (2nd version)	1960-80	◆	◆	◆	●	●
Dick Whittington (1st version)	1953-60	◆	●	●	●	●

Name	Dates					
Doc Holliday	1985-90	●	●	●	●	◆
Don Quixote	1957-91	◆	◆	◆	●	◆
Drake	1940-60	◆	◆	●	●	●
Drake (hatless version)	1940	◆	●	●	●	●
Farmer John	1938-60	◆	◆	●	●	●
Fat Boy	1940-60	●	◆	◆	◆	◆
Fireman (1st version)	1984-91	◆	●	●	●	●
Fortune Teller (1st version)	1954-67	◆	◆	◆	●	●
Fortune Teller (2nd version)	1991	◆	●	●	●	●
Friar Tuck	1951-60	◆	●	●	●	●
Gaoler	1963-83	◆	◆	◆	●	●
Gardener (1st version)	1973-80	◆	◆	◆	●	●
Gardener (2nd version)	1990-91	◆	●	●	●	●
Genie	1991	◆	●	●	●	●
George Armstrong Custer & Sitting Bull	1984	◆	●	●	●	●
George Harrison	1984-91	●	●	●	◆	◆
George Washington & King George III	1986	◆	●	●	●	●
Geronimo	1985-90	●	●	●	●	◆
Gladiator	1961-67	◆	◆	◆	●	●
Gondolier	1964-69	◆	◆	◆	●	●
Gone Away	1960-81	◆	◆	◆	●	●
Granny	1935-83	◆	◆	◆	●	●
Granny (toothless)	1935	◆	●	●	●	●
Grant & Lee	1983	◆	●	●	●	●
Groucho Marx	1984-90	◆	●	●	●	●
Guardsman	1963-83	◆	◆	◆	●	●
Gunsmith	1963-83	◆	◆	◆	●	●
Gulliver	1962-67	◆	◆	◆	●	●
Hamlet	1982-90	◆	●	●	●	●
Henry V	1982-88	◆	●	●	●	●
Henry VIII (2nd version)	1991	◆				
Izaac Walton	1952-82	◆	●	●	●	●
Jane Seymour	1979-90	◆	◆	◆	●	●
Jarge	1950-60	◆	◆	●	●	●
Jester	1936-60	●	◆	●	●	●
Jimmy Durante	1984-85	◆	●	●	●	●
Jockey (1st version)	1971-75	◆	●	●	●	●
John Barleycorn	1934-60	◆	◆	◆	●	●
John Lennon	1984-91	●	●	●	◆	
John Peel	1936-60	◆	◆	◆	◆	●
Johnny Appleseed	1953-69	◆	●	●	●	●
Juggler	1989-91	◆	●	●	●	●
King Arthur and Guinevere	1989	◆	●	●	●	●
Lobster Man	1968-91	◆	◆	◆	●	●
Lord Mayor of London	1990-91	◆	●	●	●	●
Lord Nelson	1952-69	◆	●	●	●	●
Louis Armstrong	1984-90	◆	●	●	●	●
Lumberjack	1967-82	◆	◆	P	●	●

McCallum	1935	♦	●	●	●	●
McCallum (Kingsware)	1935	♦	●	●	●	●
Macbeth	1982-90	♦	●	●	●	●
Mad Hatter	1965-83	♦	♦	♦	●	●
Mae West	1982-85	♦	●	●	●	●
The March Hare	1989	♦	●	●	●	●
Mark Twain	1980-90	♦	♦	♦	●	●
Mephistopheles	1937-48	♦	♦	●	●	●
Mikado	1959-69	♦	♦	♦	●	●
Mine Host	1958-81	♦	♦	♦	●	●
Monty	1946-91	♦	●	●	●	●
Mr Micawber	1940-60	●	♦	♦	♦	♦
Mr Pickwick	1940-60	♦	♦	♦	♦	♦
Napoleon and Josephine	1986	♦	●	●	●	●
Neptune	1961-91	♦	♦	♦	●	●
Nightwatchman	1963-83	♦	♦	♦	●	●
North American Indian	1968-91	♦	♦	♦	●	●
Old Charley	1934-83	♦	♦	♦	♦	●
Old King Cole	1939-60	♦	♦	●	●	●
Old King Cole (yellow version)	1937	♦	♦	●	●	●
Othello	1982-90	♦	●	●	●	●
Paddy	1937-60	♦	♦	♦	♦	●
Parson Brown	1935-60	♦	♦	●	●	●
Paul McCartney	1984-91	●	●	●	♦	
Pearly Boy (Brown)	1947	♦	♦	♦	♦	
Pearly Boy (Blue)	1947	♦	♦	♦	♦	
Pearly Girl (Blue)	1947	♦	♦	♦	♦	
Pearly King	1987-91	♦	●	●	●	●
Pearly Queen	1987-91	♦	●	●	●	●
Pied Piper	1954-80	♦	♦	♦	●	●
Porthos	1956-91	♦	♦	♦	●	●
Punch and Judy Man	1964-69	♦	♦	♦	●	●
Queen Victoria	1989-91	♦	●	●	●	●
The Red Queen	1988-91	♦	♦	♦	●	●
Regency Beau	1962-67	♦	♦	♦	♦	●
Ringo Starr	1984	●	●	●	♦	
Robin Hood (1st version)	1947-60	♦	♦	♦	♦	●
Robinson Crusoe	1960-82	♦	♦	♦	♦	●
Romeo	1983-90	●	●	●	●	♦
Sairey Gamp	1935-86	♦	♦	♦	♦	●
Samson and Delilah	1988	♦	●	●	●	●
Samuel Johnson	1950-60	♦	♦	●	●	●
Sam Weller	1940-50	♦	♦	♦	♦	●
Sancho Panza	1957-82	♦	♦	♦	●	●
Santa Claus (1st version)						
Santa Claus — Doll Handle	1981	♦	●	●	●	●
Santa Claus — Reindeer Handle	1982	♦	●	●	●	●
Santa Claus — Sack of Toys Handle	1983	♦	●	●	●	●
Santa Anna & Davy Crockett	1985	♦	●	●	●	●

Scaramouche (1st version)	1962-67	◆	◆	◆	●	●
Scaramouche (2nd version)	1988-91	◆	●	●	●	●
Simple Simon	1953-60	◆	●	●	●	●
Simon the Cellarer	1935-60	◆	◆	●	●	●
Sir Thomas Moore	1988-91	◆	●	●	●	●
Smuggler	1968-80	◆	●	●	●	●
Smuts	1946-48	◆	●	●	●	●
St George	1968-75	◆	◆	●	●	●
Tam O'Shanter	1973-79	◆	◆	◆	●	●
Toby Philpots	1937-69	◆	◆	◆	●	●
Tony Weller*	1936-60	◆	◆	◆	●	●
Touchstone	1936-60	◆	●	●	●	●
Town Crier (1st version)	1960-73	◆	◆	◆	●	●
Trapper	1967-82	◆	◆	P	●	●
Ugly Duchess	1965-73	◆	◆	◆	●	●
Uncle Tom Cobbleigh	1952-60	◆	●	●	●	●
Veteran Motorist	1973-83	◆	◆	◆	●	●
Vicar of Bray	1936-60	◆	●	●	●	●
Viking	1959-75	◆	◆	◆	●	●
WC Fields	1983-85	◆	●	●	●	●
Walrus & Carpenter	1965-79	◆	◆	◆	●	●
Wild Bill Hickock	1985-90	●	●	●	◆	●
William Shakespeare	1983-91	◆	●	●	●	●
Witch	1991	◆	●	●	●	●
Wyatt Earp	1985-90	●	●	●	●	◆
Yachtsman (1st version)	1971-79	◆	P	P	●	●
Yachtsman (2nd version)	1989-91	◆	●	●	●	●

* Extra large version also available   ◆ Sizes available   ● Sizes not available   P Pilot issued

Captain Hook

Discontinued Character Jug Market Values

In this book the market value of each discontinued jug is given in the form of a price range. This reflects the Doulton market where prices are known to vary around the margin on individual pieces. The very circumstances of a particular purchase may influence its price, for example, a dealer may intentionally price an item higher because he deems the collector demand in his area to be sufficient to warrant a higher sum. Another dealer could price the same item below market value in order to ensure a quick sale. The particular need for a jug may also influence its price. A collector requiring only one more piece to complete a set will place a higher value on this piece than on any of the set he already has. The result of these marginal differences in value between both collectors and dealers is that there is no fixed market price for any Doulton item. However, by collating a number of individual prices for each item it is possible to estimate the market price range. The prices given in this book are based on prices observed and collected by the author over a six-month period prior to publication.

The Doulton market changes rapidly with market values rising and falling, so always attempt to check values given with current market prices to identify changes in the market values listed in this section.

The 1960s withdrawals

Character Jug Sizes	
Tiny	1¼″ – 1½″
Miniature	2¼″ – 3″
Small	3¼″ – 4½″
Medium (New Size)	5¼″
Intermediate	4″ – 4½″
Large	5¼″ – 7¾″
Extra Large	6½″ – 7½″

Size	D.Nos	Production Dates £	Market Values $	Date Acquired	Price Paid

Airman Designer Bill Harper

A tribute to the RAF during the Second World War. A limited edition colourway of 250 in Canadian colours was produced alongside a colourway in the current range.

Size	D.Nos	Production Dates	£	$			
Small	6903	1991	£50-£60	$100-$125			☐

Anne Boleyn Designer Douglas V Tootle

Henry VIII's second wife who was beheaded by a sword at the Tower of London in 1536. The jug wrongly shows an axe rather than a sword. It is understood from Douglas Tootle that the error was in the modellers brief.

Size	D.Nos	Dates	£	$			
Large	6644	1975-90	£40-£45	$90-$95			☐
Small	6650	1980-90	£30-£35	$50-$60		18	☐
Miniature	6651	1980-90	£25-£30	$30-$40			☐

Anne of Cleves Designer M. Abberley

Henry VIII's marriage to Anne of Cleves was arranged purely for political reasons by the King's minister, Thomas Cromwell. Both King and minister were deceived by the flattering portrait of her by the court painter Hans Holbien. Henry was disappointed at her plainness and bad manners but, as he said, there was no cure he had to put his head in the yoke with the "Flanders Mare". Having said this he divorced her within a year and the unfortunate Cromwell was executed the next year. The character jug provides the unflattering comparison with the Flemish Horse. The ears down version carried on in production until 1990.

Size	D.Nos	Dates	£	$			
Large Ears Up	6653	1980-81	£70-£80	$150-$250			☐
Large	6653	1980-90	£40-£45	$90-$95			☐
Small	6753	1987-90	£25-£30	$50-$60		18	☐
Miniature	6754	1987-90	£20-£25	$30-$40			☐

Annie Oakley Designer Stan Taylor

A renowned markswoman who starred in "Buffalo Bill's Wild West Show".

Size	D.Nos	Dates	£	$			
Medium	6732	1985-89	£45-£50	$80-$90			☐

The Antique Dealer Designer Geoff Blower

Part of the Collecting World Series from Kevin Francis. A limited edition of 5000 of which only 3000 were made.

Size	D.Nos	Dates	£	$			
Large	6807	1988-91	£70-£80	$150-$175		31 00	☐

Antony &Cleopatre Designer M. Abberley
Part of the Star-Crossed Lovers Series. A limited edition of 9500.

Large	6728	1985-91	£65-£75	$140-$160	_____	_____	☐

Apothecary* Designer M. Henk
From the character jugs of Williamsburg series depicting American colonial life.
A series which has been rising in value steadily over the last few years.

Large	6567	1963-83	£60-£70	$90-$100	_____	_____	☐
Small	6574	1963-83	£35-£40	$75-$80	_____	_____	☐
Miniature	6581	1963-83	£30-£35	$60-$70	_____	_____	☐

Aramis Designer M. Henk
One of the Three Musketeers.

Large	6441	1956-91	£45-£55	$95-$110	_____	_____	☐
Small	6454	1956-91	£25-£30	$50-$65	_____	29·00	☐
Miniature	6508	1960-91	£15-£20	$40-$50	_____	_____	☐
Large	6827	1988	£55-£60	$110-$120	_____	_____	☐

'Ard of 'Earing Designer D. Biggs
From an English phrase made popular in the 1920s. This jug is the most desire 1960s
withdrawals. Commercially very unsuccessful, it has become one of the truly rare
stars of the discontinued market.

Large	6588	1964-67	£550-£600	$900-$1200	_____	_____	☐
Small	6591	1964-67	£300-£350	$750-$800	_____	_____	☐
Miniature	6594	1964-67	£375-£450	$800-$900	_____	_____	☐

'Arriet Designer H. Fenton
'Arry and 'Arriet are Cockney characters, the original Londoners with their distinctive
dialect. See Pearly Boy and Pearly Queen.

Early versions of this jug prior to 1951 have distinctive blonde hair.

Large	6208	1947-60	£110-£125	$215-$235	_____	_____	☐
Small	6236	1947-60	£60-£70	$95-$110	_____	45	☐
Miniature	6250	1947-60	£45-£50	$80-$90	_____	_____	☐
Tiny	6256	1947-60	£80-£90	$180-$200	_____	_____	☐

*Also found in bone china

'Ard of 'Earing

Apothecary

Anne Boleyn

Antony and Cleopatre

Aramis

'Arriet

'Arry Designer H. Fenton

Pre 1951 versions have a different shade of yellow on their scarf and early versions have distinctive blond hair.

Large	6207	1947-60	£110-£125	$215-$235	_____	_____	☐
Small	6235	1947-60	£60-£70	$95-$110	_____	45	☐
Miniature	6249	1947-60	£45-£50	$80-$90	_____	_____	☐
Tiny	6255	1947-60	£80-£90	$180-$200	_____	_____	☐

Athos Designer M. Henk
One of the Three Musketeers.

Large	6439	1956-91	£45-£55	$95-$110	_____	_____	☐
Small	6452	1956-91	£25-£30	$50-$65	_____	22	☐
Miniature	6509	1960-91	£15-£20	$40-$50	_____	_____	☐
Large	6827	1988	£55-£60	$110-$120	_____	_____	☐

The Auctioneer Designer G. Blower
Part of the Collecting World Series from Kevin Francis, a limited edition of 5000 of which only 2500 were made.

Large	6833	1989-91	£75-£85	$160-$180	_____	75	☐

Auld Mac/Owd Mac* Designer H. Fenton
The music-hall song about the miserly Scotsman who exclaimed "Bang went saxpence!", which Sir Harry Lauder made famous, is based on a Punch cartoon of December 5th 1868.

The caption runs: Peebles Body to townsman supposed to be in London on Business: 'E-eh, Mac! ye're sune hame again!'

Mac: E-eh, its just a ruinous place, that! Mun, a had na' been there abune twa hoours when Bang went Saxpence.'

Early versions of this jug have brown green shoulders as opposed to light green.

Large Owd Mac	5823	1937-38	£95-£100	$120-$150	_____	_____	☐
Large Auld Mac	5823	1945-85	£50-£55	$75-$85	_____	_____	☐
Small Owd Mac	5824	1938-45	£40-£45	$50-$70	_____	_____	☐
Small Auld Mac	5824	1945-85	£30-£35	$50-$70	_____	_____	☐
Mini Auld Mac	6253	1945-85	£30-£35	$25-$30	_____	_____	☐
Tiny Auld Mac	6257	1946-60	£90-£100	$225-$250	_____	_____	☐

Bacchus Designer M. Henk
The God of wine and nature in Roman mythology, associated with the pleasures of harvest celebrations.

Large	6499	1959-91	£45-£55	$95-$110	_____	_____	☐
Small	6505	1959-91	£25-£30	$50-$65	_____	_____	☐
Miniature	6521	1960-91	£15-£20	$40-$50	_____	_____	☐

Baseball Player
Pre-released in an edition of 500 to celebrate the fifth anniversary of the Miami Doulton Convention.

Small	6878	1991	£90-£100	$150-$175	_____	_____	☐
Small	6878	1991	£45-£65	$90-$100	_____	_____	☐

Beefeater Designer H. Fenton
This is the popular nickname for the Yeoman Warders of the Tower of London. Their first appearance was at the coronation of Henry VII in 1485. The derivation of the nickname has been attributed to Cosimo, Grand Duke of Tuscany who, in 1669, drew attention to their extra-large beef ration. The contingent of beefeaters is the oldest personal bodyguard still in existence.

ER Handle Version

The ER version was introduced in 1953 but the actual jug was introduced in 1947. There are two backstamp variations on the spelling of the name, plural and non-plural. An example also exists with a bottle oven backstamp in large size.

Miniature	6251	1953-91	£16-£22	$40-$50	_____	_____	☐

GR Handle Version

Large	6206	1947-53	£70-£90	$160-$180	_____	_____	☐
Small	6233	1947-53	£45-£55	$75-$85	_____	_____	☐
Miniature	6251	1947-53	£45-£55	$65-$75	_____	_____	☐
Lge Yellow Handle		1947-50s	£800-£1000	$1500-$2000	_____	_____	☐
Sml Yellow Handle		1947-50s	£700-£950	$1500-$2000	_____	_____	☐
Tiny RDICC	6806	1990	£60-£70	$120-$140	_____	_____	☐

Benjamin Franklin Designer E. Griffiths
One of America's founding fathers.

Small	6695	1982-89	£40-£45	$70-$80	_____	_____	☐

Blacksmith* Designer D. Biggs
A Williamsburg Series character from American colonial life.

Large	6571	1963-83	£60-£70	$90-$100	_____	_____	☐
Small	6578	1963-883	£40-£45	$75-$80	_____	_____	☐
Miniature	6585	1963-83	£35-£40	$60-$70	_____	_____	☐

Bootmaker* Designer D. Biggs
A Williamsburg Series character from American colonial life.

Large	6572	1963-83	£60-£70	$100-$120	_____	_____	☐
Small	6579	1963-83	£40-£45	$75-$80	_____	_____	☐
Miniature	6586	1963-83	£35-£40	$60-$70	_____	_____	☐

Buffalo Bill Designer Robert Tabbenor
The wild west buffalo hunter turned showman, William Frederick Cody (1846-1917).

Medium	6735	1985-89	£45-£40	$80-$90	_____	_____	☐

Busker Designer S. Taylor
A London street performer.

The prototype version was originally designed with a figure in the handle playing the accordion but the final model just showed an accordion.

Large	6775	1988-91	£55-£65	$95-$110	_____	_____	☐

Buz Fuz Designers L. Harradine & H. Fenton
"... with a fat body and a red face ..."

Mr Sergeant Buzfuz is the barrister for Mrs Bardell in Bardell versus Pickwick, the famous breach-of-promise suit in Charles Dickens' *The Posthumous Papers of The Pickwick Club* 1836. It is said that the character is based on one Sergeant C. C. Bompas, a London counsel of the 1830s noted for his pompous manner and his tendency to bully witnesses.

Intermediate	5838	1938-48	£85-£95	$190-$200	_____	90	☐
Small	5838	1948-60	£50-£60	$110-$130	_____	50	☐
Pick Kwick advertising jug. Limited edition of 2000							
Small		1982	£65-£75	$100-$120	_____	_____	☐

*Also found in bone china

Beefeater GR Handle

Bacchus

Auld Mac/Owd Mac

'Arry

Blacksmith

Buz Fuz

Captain Ahab* Designer G. Sharpe

Ahab: All visible objects are but as pasteboard masks"

The monomaniac captain of the whaler 'Perqual' in Herman Melville's Moby Dick or The Whale" 1851. His single obsession is the capture of the fierce and cunning white whale Moby Dick which tore away his leg on a previous encounter. The book culminates in a three day struggle with the whale in which the captain's ivory leg is snapped off and he is pinioned to the animal by the harpoon rope. This tale of inexorable fate and of good and evil is based partly on reports of Mocha-Dick, a white whale which sustained 19 harpoons, caused 30 deaths, stove 3 whaling ships and sunk 16 vessels.

Large	6500	1959-84	£50-£60	$85-$90	————	————	☐
Small	6506	1959-84	£30-£40	$45-$55	————	_30_	☐
Miniature	6522	1959-84	£30-£35	$35-$45	————	————	☐

Captain Henry Morgan* Designer G. Sharpe

Described by George Wycherley as a "depraved, vicious, treacherous, almost unparalleled human brute, who was born of respectable people in Wales but deliberately chose the most evil life possible in his vicious age".

Transported to the West Indies as a young man, Morgan escaped from enforced plantation work, and became a pirate. In 1671 he led a band of 2000 English and French pirates against the rich port of Panama. After sacking the city, Morgan returned to the Caribbean and made off with most of the loot. He was then knighted by Charles II and appointed Lieutenant Governor of Jamaica. Then, under the King's orders he proceeded to hang every pirate he could find, including his former henchmen.

Large	6467	1958-81	£60-£70	$80-$90	————	————	☐
Small	6469	1958-81	£35-£45	$60-$70	————	_30_	☐
Miniature	6510	1960-81	£30-£35	$40-$50	————	————	☐

Captain Hook* Designers M. Henk & D. Biggs

Captain Hook from Peter Pan by J. M. Barrie.

One of the desirable 60s set.

Large	6597	1965-71	£250-£275	$400-$450	————	————	☐
Small	6601	1965-71	£150-£170	$325-$350	————	————	☐
Miniature	6605	1965-71	£125-£140	$325-$375	————	————	☐

Captain Cuttle Designers L. Harradine & H. Fenton

Captain Edward Cuttle from Dickens' *Dombey and Son* 1846. Had been a pilot or skipper, or privateers-man, or all three perhaps; and was a very salt looking man in deed. "his favourite saying is: When found, make a note of."

Two colour versions exist one with a green hat and one with a brown hat

Intermediate	5842	1938-48	£95-£105	$200-$220	————	_80_	☐
Small	5842	1948-60	£60-£70	$100-$110	————	_42_	☐

Cardinal Designer C. J. Noke

One of the princes of the church constituting the sacred college at Rome which elects each new Pope. The name derives from the Latin for hinge hence 'of fundamental importance.'

There are three hair colour changes known to exist; brown, grey and white. The brown hair version is dated 1938 while the grey and white versions carry a mark dating them from the 1950s.

Large	5614	1936-60	£75-£85	$130-$150	_____		☐
Small	6033	1939-60	£40-£45	$80-$90	_____	4 0	☐
Miniature	6129	1940-60	£35-£40	$60-$70	_____		☐
Tiny	6258	1947-60	£80-£90	$225-$250	_____		☐

Catherine of Aragon Designer A. Maslankowski

The first of Henry VIII's wives whose subsequent marriage annulment led directly to the British break with Catholicism.

Large	6643	1975-89	£40-£45	$90-$95	_____		☐
Small	6657	1981-89	£30-£35	$50-$60	_____		☐
Miniature	6658	1981-89	£25-£30	$30-$40	_____		☐

Catherine Howard Designer Peter Gee

The fifth wife of Henry VIII who was beheaded at the Tower of London in 1541.

Large	6645	1978-89	£40-£50	$95-$100	_____		☐
Small	6692	1984-89	£35-£40	$55-$65	_____		☐
Miniature	6693	1984-89	£30-£35	$35-$45	_____		☐

Catherine Parr Designer M. Abberley

The last of Henry VIII's wives, one who actually survived him

Large	6664	1981-89	£40-£50	$95-$100	_____		☐
Small	6751	1987-89	£30-£40	$55-$65	_____		☐
Miniature	6752	1987-89	£30-£35	$35-$45	_____		☐

Cavalier Designer H. Fenton

Originally a form of abuse, implying an overbearing manner, 'cavalier' was adopted by the Royalists during the Civil War to describe themselves. Cavaliers were opposed to the Roundheads of Cromwell and the Parliamentarians.

"God for King Charles! Pym and such carles.

To the devil that prompts 'em their treasonous parles!"

Early versions prior to 1950 have a different shade of green on their hat.

Large	6114	1940-60	£60-£65	$125-$140	_____		☐
Small	6173	1941-60	£40-£45	$70-$80	_____	3 5	☐
Lge Goatee	6114	1940-42	£1400-£1800	$3000-$4000	_____		☐

Chelsea Pensioner Designer S. Taylor

The old soldiers living in the Chelsea Royal Hospital who look quite splendid in their dress uniform when seen in London.

Pre-released in 4 backstamp editions of 250 each in 1988. All versions are large.

	6817	1989-91	£50-£60	$120-$140	_____	_____	☐
J Horne	6830	1988	£80-£100	$180-$220	_____	_____	☐
D H Holmes	6831	1988	£80-£100	$180-$220	_____	_____	☐
Higbee	6832	1988	£80-£100	$180-$220	_____	_____	☐
S & Clothier	6833	1988	£80-£100	$180-$220	_____	_____	☐

City Gent Designer S. Taylor

The 1920s British gentleman working in the Stock Exchange or some other part of the Establishment.

Large	6815	1988-91	£50-£60	$95-$110	_____	_____	☐

Churchill Designer (First Version) C. J. Noke

War leader, statesman, soldier, journalist, orator, painter and bricklayer.

"Don't talk to me about naval tradition. Its nothing but rum, buggery and the lash"

"All the good things are simple, and many can be expressed in a single word: freedom; justice; honour; duty; mercy; hope."

Three coloured versions are known to exist in two variations. One sold in 1990 for £16,000.

Large	6170	1940	£2500-£3000	$7000-$8000	_____	_____	☐

Clark Gable Designer S. Taylor

Once asked by a magazine writer:
"How does it feel to be the screen's greatest lover?"
The five-times-married Hollywood star replied:
"It's a living."

This jug was withdrawn due to copyright problems. Less than 500 are known to exist.

Large	6709	1984	£1500-£2000	$3000-$4000	_____	_____	☐

Clown (First Version) Designer H. Fenton

A comic character from the circus.

Large (Red hair)	5610	1937-42	£750-£850	$2000-$2700	_____	_____	☐
Large (Brown hair)	5610	1937-42	£750-£850	$2000-$2700	_____	_____	☐
Large (White hair)	6322	1951-55	£400-£500	$1000-$1200	_____	_____	☐
Pilot Black hair		1938	Value impossible to determine				

Cardinal

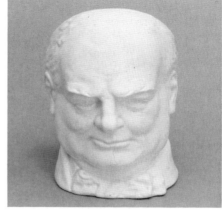

Churchill

Captain Cuttle

Captain Hook

Catherine of Aragon

Red Haired Clown

The Collector Designers S. Taylor and G. Blower
The first in the Collecting World Series from Kevin Francis.

Large	6796	1988-90	£80-£95	$175-$225	_____	75	☐

Cook &Cheshire Cat Designer W.Harper
From the Alice in Wonderland Series.

Large	6842	1990-91	£65-£75	$130-$150	_____	_____	☐

D'Artagnan Designer S. Taylor
The fourth member of the Three Musketeers from the book by Alexandre Dumas.

Miniature	6765	1987-91	£15-£20	$40-$50	_____	_____	☐

Dick Turpin (First Version) Designers C. J. Noke & H. Fenton
During a short but eventful life, 1705-39, Turpin was a butcher's apprentice, then a cattle thief, smuggler, housebreaker, horse thief and a notorious highwayman. He was executed in 1739 and actually paid 5 men £3 10s to mourn at the event.

Early versions have the initials RT on the butt of the pistol.

Large	5485	1935-60	£70-£80	$130-$140	_____	_____	☐
Small	5618	1936-60	£40-£45	$75-$85	_____	_____	☐
Miniature	6128	1940-60	£30-£35	$50-$60	_____	_____	☐

Dick Turpin* (Second Version) Designer D. Biggs
This version wears a mask and a horse shaped handle.

Large	6528	1960-80	£50-£60	$70-$80	_____	_____	☐
Small	5635	1960-80	£35-£40	$55-$65	_____	18	☐
Miniature	6542	1960-80	£25-£30	$35-$45	_____	_____	☐

Dick Whittington (First Version)Designer G. Blower
The legend of Dick Whittington dates from 1605 and is a complete fabrication. In actual fact he began as a mercer in London and sold cloth to Henry Bolingbroke who was later King Henry IV. He was to serve four terms as the Mayor of London in the 14th century thanks to certain patronages.

Large	6375	1953-60	£170-£190	$375-$400	_____	_____	☐

Doc Holliday Designer S. Taylor
Part of the Wild West Collection.

Medium	6731	1985-89	£45-£50	$80-940	_____	_____	☐

Don Quixote Designer G. Blower
From the novel by Cervantes.

Large	6455	1957-91	£30-£35	$50-$60	_____	_____	☐
Small	6460	1957-91	£15-£20	$30-$40	_____	_____	☐
Miniature	6511	1960-91	£10-£15	$20-$30	_____	_____	☐

Drake (First Version) Designer H. Fenton
He was the first Englishman to circumnavigate the globe 1577-80. In 1587, he led the daring raid on Cadiz, the famous "singeing of the King of Spain's beard." He was known as El Draco amongst the Spanish whom he terrorised and whom he helped defeat in 1588 at the great rout of the Armada.

Large	6115	1940-60	£75-£85	$140-$150	_____	_____	☐
Small	6174	1941-60	£45-£55	$90-$100	_____	40	☐
Lge Hatless		1940-41	£1300-£1700	$4000-$5000	_____	_____	☐

Drake (Second Version) Designer P. Gee
Special edition of 6000. Commissioned by the Guild to celebrate the 400th anniversary of the Armada

Large	6805	1988-9	_____	_____	☐

Falconer Designer M. Henk
The hunter with his bird taking part in the sport of kings.
Large version was produced as a limited edition of 250 and 1000

Large (250)	6798	1987	£65-£75	$120-$140	_____	_____	☐
Large (1000)	6800	1988	£45-£55	$95-$110	_____	_____	☐
Miniature	6547	1960-61	£15-£20	$40-$50	_____	_____	☐

Falstaff Designer H. Fenton
A character from Shakespeare's Henry IV. A portly amusing braggart fond of a drink.
Colour trials are known to exist in all sizes of this jug including the current versions.

Large	6797	1987	£50-£60	$100-$120	_____	_____	☐
Miniature	6519	1960-61	£15-£20	$40-$50	_____	_____	☐

*Also found in bone china

Farmer John Designer C. J. Noke

A cartoon from "Punch" 1889 had the following caption:

"Landlord: 'Well … at any rate you've got a magnificent crop of hay this —'

Portly Tenant Farmer reluctantly:

'Ye-es; but you see, my lord, there's such a precious lot of it! Look what it'll cost me for labour to get it in.'"

Early version has the handle entering the top of the jug and is worth slightly more. See Backstamp variations.

| Large | 5788 | 1938-60 | £70-£80 | $150-$160 | | | ☐ |
| Small | 5789 | 1938-60 | £45-£50 | $80-$90 | | 40 | ☐ |

Fat Boy Designers L. Harradine & H. Fenton

The enormous Joe from The Pickwick Papers by Dickens says: "I wants to make your flesh creep".

The murderer Charles Pearce claimed to be the original on whom Joe was based but James Budden, son of the Landlord of the Red Lion Inn at Chatham in Kent, is more likely.

Intermediate	5840	1938-48	£90-£100	$175-$195		85	☐
Small	5840	1948-60	£55-£70	$120-$140			☐
Miniature	6139	1940-60	£40-£45	$70-$80			☐
Tiny	6142	1940-60	£55-£65	$95-$110			☐

Fireman Designer R. Tabbenor

Commissioned and pre-released in 1983 by Griffiths Pottery House with a special backstamp.

| Large | 6697 | 1984-91 | £50-£60 | $90-$110 | | | ☐ |

Fortune Teller (First Version) Designer G. Sharpe

"Show me a rich fortune-teller" — proverbial.

Large	6497	1959-67	£240-£260	$475-$500			☐
Small	6503	1959-67	£150-£170	$300-$350			☐
Miniature	6523	1960-67	£135-£160	$375-$425			☐

Fortune Teller (Second Version) Designer S. Taylor

The 1991 Character Jug of the Year. Only produced for 12 months.

| Large | 6874 | 1991 | £65-£75 | $125-$150 | | | ☐ |

Fortune Teller

Fat Boy

Falstaff

Dick Turpin (Second Version)

The Collector

Drake (First Version)

Friar Tuck Designer H. Fenton

The rotund monk and swordsman — one of Robin Hood's Merry Men.

Large	6321	1951-60	£170-£190	$400-$425	_____	_____	☐

Gaoler* Designer D. Biggs

Another Williamsburg Series character from American colonial life.

Large	6570	1963-83	£60-£70	$80-$90	_____	_____	☐
Small	6577	1963-83	£35-£40	$40-$50	_____	_____	☐
Miniature	6584	1963-83	£30-£35	$30-$40	_____	_____	☐

Gardener (First Version) Designer D. Biggs

Gardening the purest of human pleasures … the greatest refreshment to the spirits of man; without which, buildings and palaces are but gross handiworks.

Early versions have a brown coloured hat as distinct to green. A jug which has greatly appreciated in value in recent years, it is expected to go further.

Large	6630	1973-80	£140-£160	$200-$240	_____	_____	☐
Small	6634	1973-80	£70-£80	$70-$80	_____	_55_	☐
Miniature	6638	1973-80	£50-£60	$50-$60	_____	_____	☐

Gardener (Second Version) Designer S. Taylor

Large	6868	1990-91	£55-£65	$100-$125	_____	_____	☐
Small	6867	1990	£RRP	$RRP	_____	_____	☐

Genie Designer S.Taylor

With a production run of only six months this jug should become one of the most sought after of the 1991 withdrawals. It's ugly enough to become the 'Ard of 'Earing of the 90s.

Large	6892	1991	£85-£95	$160-$180	_____	☐

George Armstrong Custer and Sitting Bull

Designer M. Abberley

General Custer and 250 of the 7th US Cavalry died heroically at the Battle of the Little Big Horn June 26th 1876. For the Sioux Indians, led by chiefs Sitting Bull and Crazy Horse, the victory was to be a futile one since the relentless advance of the paleface was unstoppable.

The second in the Antagonists series. A limited edition of 9500 now sold out. There are two versions of this jug identical but for the colour of Sitting Bull's eyes, one versions are brown while the other is grey-blue.

Large	6712	1984	£70-£80	$140-$160	_____	☐

George Harrison Designer Stan Taylor

One of the Beatles. Not originally viewed as musical, his credentials are now well established. He also proved himself in the film world being responsible for "The Life of Brian" amongst others.

Medium	6727	1984-91	£30-£35	$80-$100			☐

George Washington Designer S. Taylor

The first president of the United States in 1789, and one of the founding fathers of the nation.

The jug was given a commemorative backstamp for 1989 to celebrate the 200th Anniversary of the election of the first president of America. The backstamp is not found on the miniature size.

Small	6824	1989-91	£25-£30	$45-$55			☐
Miniature	6825	1989-91	£15-£20	$40-$50			☐

George Washington and King George III

Designer Michael Abberley

Number 4 in the Antagonists Series.

Large	6749	1986	£60-£70	$100-$120			☐

Geronimo Designer Stan Taylor

A famous leader of the Apache Indians who finally surrendered in 1886. The rarest of the Wild West series

Medium	6733	1985-1988	£55-£60	$100-$140			☐

Gladiator Designer M. Henk

These professional fighting men were recruited from condemned criminals and prisoners of war. They fought for public entertainment in the amphitheatres of Ancient Rome until the spectacle was forbidden by the Emperor Honorius in AD 404 after a monk, Telemachus, attempted to stop the combat and was torn to pieces by the angry crowd. Successful Gladiators received great rewards such as their freedom and some became popular idols, like the Thracian Celadus who is described in graffiti in Pompeii as "decus puellarum, expirium puellarum" 'boys' hero, girls' heart-throb'.

Large	6550	1961-67	£300-£320	$550-$600			☐
Small	6553	1961-67	£185-£210	$350-$375			☐
Miniature	6556	1961-67	£180-£200	$375-$425			☐

*Also found in bone china

Golfer (First Version) Designer D. Biggs
Large version produced as a Colourway

Large	6784	1987-89	£40-£50	$95-$110	_____	_____	☐
Small	6756	1986-91	£25-£30	$45-$55	_____	_____	☐
Miniature	6757	1986-91	£15-£20	$35-$45	_____	_____	☐

Gondolier* Designer D. Biggs
Robert Benchley once cabled Harold Ross, editor of the *New Yorker*, from Venice: "Streets full of water. Please advise". He need not have worried about transport. Like the punt, the gondola is one of the few craft which are propelled standing up. Boat racing began in Venice — the Venetian 'regatta' of 1300 featured a gondola race.

Large	6589	1964-69	£225-£275	$525-$575	_____	_____	☐
Small	6592	1964-69	£165-£200	$400-$450	_____	_____	☐
Miniature	6595	1964-69	£140-£160	$350-$400	_____	_____	☐

Gone Away* Designer G. Sharpe
The traditional hunting cry used when the scent of the fox has been lost. The huntsman is shown in his distinctive pink coat as if to embark on another slaughter of defenceless animals. "It is very strange and very melancholy that the paucity of human pleasures should persuade us ever to call hunting one of them" a remark made by Dr Johnson.

Large	6531	1960-81	£50-£60	$80-$90	_____	_____	☐
Small	6538	1960-81	£30-£35	$40-$50	_____	18	☐
Miniature	6545	1960-81	£25-£30	$40-$50	_____	_____	☐

Granny* Designers M. Fenton & M. Henk
Depicts a traditional old Granny.

Large	5521	1935-83	£55-£65	$80-$100	_____	_____	☐
Small	6384	1953-83	£35-£45	$70-$80	_____	18	☐
Miniature	6520	1960-83	£25-£30	$50-$60	_____	_____	☐

Granny (Toothless Version) Designers H. Fenton & M. Henk
Depicts an ancient toothless crone.

An early mould variation of the Granny.

Large	5521	1934-40	£350-£450	$800-$1000	_____	_____	☐

*Also found in bone china

Gone Away

Gaoler

George Washington and King George III

Granny (Both Versions)

George Armstrong Custer

Sitting Bull

Grant and Lee Designer M. Abberley

Two opposing generals from the American Civil War. Produced as a limited edition of 9,500. A colour variation with reverse colours on the handle sold for £1500 in 1986. This is a prototype of the original jug and was made in a china body. Another jug which has risen steadily in the last year and one which is likely to rise further.

| Large | 6698 | 1983 | £160-£200 | $225-$275 | | | ☐ |

Groucho Marx Designer Stan Taylor

One of the great American comics whose films have become classics.

Part of the Celebrity Collection.

| Large | 6710 | 1984-88 | £60-£70 | $100-$120 | | | ☐ |

Guardsman* (First Version) Designer M. Henk

A character from the Williamsburg Series of American colonial life.

Large	6568	1963-83	£60-£70	$80-$90			☐
Small	6575	1963-83	£35-£40	$45-$55			☐
Miniature	6582	1963-83	£30-£35	$40-$50			☐

Guardsman (Second Version) Designer S. Taylor

This version represents the famous guards that are stationed outside Buckingham Palace. Part of the London Collection still produced in large and small size. A prototype handle with a Union Jack is known to exist in the large size.

| Miniature | 6772 | 1987-91 | £15-£20 | $40-$50 | | | ☐ |

Gulliver Designer D. Biggs

The central character from the book, *Gulliver's Travels*, published in 1726.

Large	6560	1962-67	£260-£300	$550-$600			☐
Small	6563	1962-67	£150-£170	$350-$370			☐
Miniature	6566	1962-67	£180-£200	$400-$425			☐

Gunsmith* Designer D. Biggs

A character from the Williamsburg Series of American Colonial life.

Large	6573	1963-83	£60-£70	$80-$90			☐
Small	6580	1963-83	£35-£40	$45-$55			☐
Miniature	6587	1963-83	£30-£35	$30-$35			☐

*Also found in bone china

Hamlet Designer M. Abberley
One of Shakespeare's characters.

Large	D6672	1982-89	£60-£70	$100-$120			☐

The Hampshire Cricketer Designer H. Sales
Limited edition of 5000.

Medium	6739	1985	£50-£60	$80-$110		40	☐

Henry V Designer R. Tabbenor
From the Shakespearean collection.

Earlier editions have raised decoration on the handle and are worth slightly more.

Large	6671	1982-89	£65-£75	$100-$120			☐

Henry VIII (Second Version) Designer W. Harper
A superb limited edition which has initially proved very successful. The first two handled jug since the 1940 Winston Churchill. An edition of 1991.

Large	6888	1991	£200-£250	$4100-$500			☐

Izaac Walton* Designer G. Blower
He was a writer of biographies and was the first to realise the importance of letters in researching biography. However he is best known for "The Compleat Angler" a collection of songs, verses, anecdotes and recipes, full of pastoral charm.

"No man is born an artist nor an angler".

Large	6404	1953-82	£65-£70	$90-$110			☐

Jane Seymour Designer Michael Abberley
The third wife of Henry VIII who produced the hoped for son but tragically died soon afterwards.

Large	6646	1979-90	£40-£50	$95-$100			☐
Small	6746	1986-90	£35-£40	$55-$65		18	☐
Miniature	6747	1986-90	£30-£35	$35-$45			☐

Jarge Designer H. Fenton
Depicts a typical country bumpkin. The forelock on some versions is painted red as distinct to the normal orange colour found on its hair.

Large	6288	1950-60	£150-£170	$300-$325			☐
Small	6295	1950-60	£70-£80	$200-$225		21	☐

Jester Designer C. J. Noke

The medieval fool of the court.

In some jugs the colours of the bobbles of the hat are reversed.

Small	5556	1936-60	£55-£65	$120-$130	_____	_____	☐

Jimmy Durante Designer D. Biggs

An American cabaret artist and film star. With such a short production life this jug seems set to appreciate rapidly.

Large	6708	1985-86	£80-£90	$140-$160	_____	_____	☐

Jockey* (First Version) Designer D. Biggs

A horse rider in British horse racing. One of the two small pilots known turned up at a local Stoke auctioneer and initially sold for only £10.00.

Large	6625	1971-75	£175-£190	$325-$350	_____	_____	☐
Small	Pilot	Early 70s	£1500-£2000	$3000-$4000	_____	_____	☐

John Barleycorn Designer C. J. Noke

Colloquial personification of barley, corn and beer. He is described in an anonymous English ballad, usually sung to the tune of "We plough the fields and scatter".

"And the huntsman he can't hunt the fox,
Nor so loudly blow his horn,
And the tinker he can't mend kettles or pots
Without a little of Barleycorn."

Early version has the handle entering the top of the jug and is valued slightly more on the market. This was the first jug released by Royal Doulton.

Large	5327	1933-60	£80-£90	$140-$160	_____	_____	☐
Small	5735	1937-60	£50-£60	$80-$90	_____	_____	☐
Miniature	6041	1939-60	£40-£55	$65-$75	_____	_____	☐
Special Edition limited to 7500 issued in 1978 black handle and special backstamp							
Large		1978	£70-£80	$140-$160	_____	_____	☐
Amex	6780	1988	£90-£100	$250-$300	_____	_____	

John Doulton Designer E Griffiths

The founder of the Doulton Pottery. Issued to Collectors Club members upon joining the club.

Version one, 8 o'clock on the clockface and dark brown eyes.							
Version two, 2 o'clock on the clockface and grey eyes.							
Small	6656	1981	£60-£70	$120-$160	_____	_____	☐
Version 2			£40-£50	$100-$120	_____	20	☐

Grant

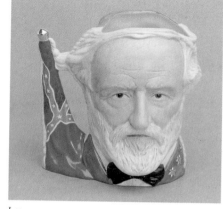

Lee

Guardsman (First Version)

Guardsman (Second Version)

Jester

Gulliver

John Lennon Designer S. Taylor

The musical genius behind the Beatles. Tragically assassinated in 1980. Limited edition colourway of 1000 also produced by John Sinclair

Medium	6725	1984-91	£30-£35	$80-$100	_____	_____	☐
Medium	6797	1987	£90-120	$200-$300	_____	_____	☐

John Peel Designer H. Fenton

A famous huntsman who lived between 1776 and 1854. The ultimate sexist pig he apparently lived for the saddle and for the drinking parties held after every hunt. This seems to have been his sole occupation through life and little is known about his long suffering wife apart from the fact that he eloped with her to Gretna Green.

The band on the handle is found in both orange and grey, the grey being more common. See horn handle version in rarities section.

Large	5612	1936-60	£75-£85	$140-$160	_____	_____	☐
Small	5731	1937-60	£40-£50	$75-$85	_____	_____	☐
Miniature	6130	1940-60	£35-£49	$55-$65	_____	_____	☐
Tiny	6259	1947-60	£90-£110	$240-$260	_____	_____	☐

Johnny Appleseed* Designer H. Fenton

An American folk hero.

This was the soubriquet of John Chapman 1774-1847 a orchardist who planted fruit trees for frontier settlers in Pennsylvania, Ohio, Indianna and Illinois.

"Reproofs for men who build the world like moles,
Models for men, if they would build the world
As Johnney Appleseed would have it done
Praying, and reading the book of Swedenborg
On the mountain-top called 'Going-To-The-Sun'."

From a ballad by V. Lindsay.

Large	6372	1953-69	£175-£200	$190-$210	_____	_____	☐

Juggler Designer S. Taylor

The popular circus act.

Large	6835	1989-91	£60-£70	$130-$150	_____	_____	☐

King Arthur &Guinevere Designer S. Taylor

Part of the Star-Crossed Lovers series. A limited edition of 9500.

Large	6836	1989-91	£60-£70	$130-$150	_____	_____	☐

King Phillip II Designer W.Harper

Commissioned by Lawleys by post to celebrate the 400th anniversary of the Armada. A limited edition of 8500.

Small	6822	1988	£30-£40	$80-$90			

Lawyer Designer M Henk

Representing the British legal system and portraying a solicitor in his court clothes and grey wig.

Miniature	6524	1960-91	£15-£20	$35-$40			

Lobster Man Designer D. Biggs

Between 1987 and 1989 a colourway was introduced in the large size.

Large	6617	1968-91	£45-£55	$80-$90			
Small	6620	1968-91	£25-£30	$55-$65			
Miniature	6652	1980-91	£15-£20	$45-$55			
Colourway	6783	1987-89	£50-£60	$90-$110			

London Bobby Designer S. Taylor

The London policeman referred to as bobbies. *Early versions have a raised decal on the badge while later versions have a flat transfer.*

Miniature	6763	1987-91	£15-£20	$40-$50			

Long John Silver Designer M. Henk

The pirate from Robert Louis Stevenson's *Treasure Island* who with Jim Hawkins set off to seek buried treasure.

Large size was commissioned in an limited edition of 250.

Large	5799	1987	£50-£60	$90-$110			
Miniature	6512	1960-91	£15-£20	$40-$50			

Lord Mayor of London Designer S. Taylor

Resplendent in his rich gown and with elaborate staff the Lord Mayor is honoured every year in London with a parade through the streets.

Large	6864	1990-91	£55-£65	$110-$130			

*Also found in bone china

Lord Nelson* Designer G. Blower

Admiral Nelson, England's greatest naval hero. Throughout his life he avoided having full-length portraits of him painted due to his sensitivity about his height. After the Battle of the Nile, in 1798, he was presented with a coffin made from the mast of the defeated French Admiral's flagship and he kept it in his cabin in the "Victory" at all times. After the Battle of Trafalgar, in 1805, Nelson's body was preserved in rum the so called "Nelson's Blood" for the journey back to England.

See Special Backstamps section.

Large	6336	1952-69	£180-£200	$325-$350	_____	_____	☐

Louis Armstrong Designer D. Biggs

One of America's greatest jazz musicians. Part of the Celebrity series. A good future investment jug for all the wrong reasons.

Large	6707	1984-88	£60-£70	$100-$120	_____	_____	☐

Lumberjack* Designer M. Henk

Depicts a North American lumberjack.

Large	6610	1967-82	£60-£70	$75-$85	_____	_____	☐
Small	6613	1967-82	£25-£30	$45-$55	_____	3 0	☐
Miniature	Pilot	Unknown	£700-£1100	$1800-$2000	_____	_____	☐
Large Canadian Centennial Backstamp							
Large	6610	1967	£90-£110	$300-$400	_____	_____	☐

Macbeth Designer Michael Abberley

Part of the Shakespearean Collection. *A number of handle prototypes are known to exist.*

Large	6667	1982-89	£60-£70	$100-$120	_____	_____	☐

Mad Hatter* Designer M. Henk

Taken from *Alice in Wonderland*. The character was based on one Theophilus Carter, an Oxford furniture dealer who wore his hat on the back of his head like the Mad Hatter. Similarly preoccupied with time, he invented an Alarm Clock Bed which tipped its occupant out at the appointed time. This was exhibited at the 1851 Great Exhibition.

"If you knew time as well as I do," said the Hatter, "you wouldn't talk about wasting it. It's him."

Mad as a hatter — the origin of this phrase is the use of mercurous nitrate in the making of felt hats. The chemical can induce chorea or 'St Vitus' Dance' in human beings — a nervous disease causing involuntary movements of the face or limbs.

Large	6598	1965-83	£70-£80	$140-$160	_____	_____	☐
Small	6602	1965-83	£45-£50	$50-$60	_____	_____	☐
Miniature	6606	1965-83	£40-£45	$40-$50	_____	_____	☐

Lumberjack

Mad Hatter

Louis Armstrong

London Bobby

Long John Silver

John Lennon

Limited Editions produced for Higbee

Large	6748	1985		_____ _____	☐
Small	6790	1985		_____ _____	☐

Mae West Designer C. Davidson

"Is that a pistol in your pocket or are you pleased to see me". An actress renowned for her risque one-liners.

A few versions have no eyebrows which makes no difference to value. 500 were produced for American Express with a promotional backstamp.

Large	6688	1983-85	£70-£80	$110-$140	_____ _____	☐
Amex	6688	1983	£125-£150	$300-$500	_____ _____	☐

The March Hare Designer W. Harper

From the Alice in Wonderland Series. Alice meets the March Hare whose life is made up of a continuous teatime with his friend the Dormouse. This jug represented quite a departure for Doulton as it represents the first animal character jug in the range.

Large	6776	1989-91	£65-£75	$120-$140	_____ _____	☐

Mark Twain Designer E. Griffiths

A classic American author of *Tom Sawyer* and *Huckleberry Finn*.

Large	6654	1980-90	£40-£45	$80-$100	_____ _____	☐
Small	6694	1983-90	£25-£30	$45-$55	_____ _____	☐
Miniature	6758	1986-90	£25-£30	$40-$50	_____ _____	☐

Mephistopheles Designers C. J. Noke & H. Fenton

From the medieval legend by Faust. *A rhyme backstamp sells at a slight premium. See Collector character jug.*

Large	5757	1937-48	£1100-£1250	$2000-$2200	_____ _____	☐
Small	5758	1937-48	£450-£500	$950-$1050	_____ _____	☐

Merlin Designer G.Sharpe

From the legend of King Arthur and the Knights of the Round Table. Merlin was the Court Wizard to King Arthur.

Miniature	6543	1960-91	£15-£20	$40-$50	_____ _____	☐

Michael Doulton Designer Bill Harper

A descendant of John Doulton used as a promotional figure by the company today. This jug was only available at promotional events at retailers.

Small	6808	1988-90	£20-£25	$45-$55	_____ _____	☐

Mikado* Designer M. Henk

Title of the emperors of Japan, now little used. The last incumbent, Hirohito (1901-1990) was 124th in a line which begins in the fourth century. He became Emperor in 1926 but formally gave up any claim to divinity in 1946, becoming a fully constitutional monarch. A fellow of the Royal Society, he published nine books on botany and marine biology.

On the small size jug the moustache is occasionally missing, this makes no difference to the jug's value.

Large	6501	1959-69	£200-£220	$400-$450			☐
Small	6507	1959-69	£125-£150	$290-$330			☐
Miniature	6525	1960-69	£120-£130	$275-$325			☐

Mine Host* Designer M. Henk

A merry 'old English' landlord.

Large	6468	1958-81	£55-£65	$75-$85			☐
Small	6470	1958-81	£35-£40	$45-$50			☐
Miniature	6513	1960-81	£30-£35	$35-$45			☐

Mr Micawber Designers L. Harradine & H. Fenton

The agent for Mordstone and Grinby in Dickens' *David Copperfield*. The character was based partly on the author's father.

"A stoutish middle-aged person in a brown surtout and black tights and shoes, with no more hair upon his head which was a huge one and very shining than there is upon an egg, and a very extensive face."

Intermediate	5843	1938-48	£85-£95	$150-$170			☐
Small	5843	1948-60	£40-£45	$100-$110		3 8	☐
Miniature	6138	1940-60	£35-£40	$50-$60			☐
Tiny	6143	1940-60	£55-£60	$95-$110			☐
Small Pick Kwik Advertising Jug limited to 2000							
Small		1984	£40-£50	$90-$120			☐

Mr Pickwick Designers L. Harradine & H. Fenton

General chairman and founder of the Pickwick club. "I am ruminating," said Mr Pickwick, "on the strange mutability of human affairs'.' Dickens spotted the name for his central character on the door of a coach at the White Hart Hotel, Bath.

The small size jug has the handle on the back and slightly different features as adopted by Harry Fenton.

Large	6060	1940-60	£85-£95	$160-$180			☐
Intermediate	5839	1938-48	£70-£80	$150-$175		60	☐
Small	5839	1948-60	£40-£45	$75-$85		35	☐
Miniature	6254	1947-60	£35-£40	$65-$75			☐
Tiny	6260	1947-60	£85-£95	$210-$230			☐

Small Pick Kwik Advertising Jug limited to 2000

Whisky bottle handle	1981	£65-£75	$100-$120	_____	_____	☐
Jim Beam handle	1983	£65-£75	$100-$120	_____	_____	☐

Mr Quaker Designer H. Sales

An advertising jug commissioned by Quaker Oats in a limited edition of 3500. Very few were made available to collectors, with the bulk being used for promotional purposes.

Large	6738	1985	£200-£225	$450-$500	_____	_____	☐

Monty (Early colour change version) Designer H. Fenton

The troops' popular name for Field Marshal Viscount Montgomery of Alamein. He was the only soldier entitled to wear two badges on his beret: one for the Tank Corps and another denoting General's rank.

In defeat, unbeatable; in victory, unbearable." — Churchill.

Earlier versions have light yellow brown as opposed to green brown shoulders of the current model. The badge background colour is also different.

Large	6202	1946-91	£50-£60	$70-$80	_____	_____	☐

Montgomery of Alamein Designer S. Taylor

Britain's leading general in World War Two and the leader of the "Desert Rats" who achieved a victory over Rommell's forces in North Africa. A limited edition of 2500, issued by Royal Doulton.

Large	6548	1961-91	£30-£40	$60-$70	_____	_____	☐
Small	6552	1961-91	£20-£25	$30-$40	_____	_____	☐
Miniature	6555	1961-91	£15-£20	$25-$30	_____	_____	☐

Napoleon & Josephine Designer M. Abberley

The second in the Star Crossed Lovers series with a limited edition of 9500. Not fully sold out. A collector case of "Not tonight Josephine".

Large	6750	1986	£60-£70	$100-$125	_____	_____	☐

Neptune Designer G. Blower

The god of the sea in Roman mythology.

Large	6548	1961-91	£30-£40	$60-$70	_____	_____	☐
Small	6552	1961-91	£20-£25	$30-$40	_____	_____	☐
Miniature	6555	1961-91	£15-£20	$25-$30	_____	_____	☐

*Also found in bone china

Montgomery of Alamein

Mikado

Merlin

Mephistopheles

Michael Doulton

Neptune

Night Watchman* Designer M. Henk
A Williamsburg Series character from American colonial life.

Large	6569	1963-83	£60-£70	$80-$90	_____	_____	☐
Small	6576	1963-83	£30-£40	$45-$50	_____	_____	☐
Miniature	6583	1963-83	£30-£35	$35-$40	_____	_____	☐

North American Indian (Canadian Centennial)
Designer M. Henk

The ancestors of today's North American Indians travelled across a land bridge between what is now the eastern extreme of the Soviet Union and Alaska, many thousands of years ago. The 'scalping' for which they were so feared in the nineteenth century was actually started by the European settlers, who forced the formerly peaceful Indian tribes off their land and on to the plains of America's Mid-West.

Issued with a special backstamp for the Canadian Centennial.

Large	6611	1967	£90-£100	$300-$350	_____	_____	☐
Large	6611	1967-91	£30-£40	$60-$70	_____	_____	☐
Small	6614	1967-91	£20-£40	$30-$40	_____	_____	☐
Miniature	6665	1981-91	£15-20	$25-$30	_____	_____	☐
Special Colourway							
Large	6786	1987			_____	_____	☐

Old Charley* Designer C. J. Noke
Known to exist in the large size with grey hair and larger blue spots on his bow tie. The popular character appears in more sizes and derivatives than any other. 15 different items are available for the dedicated collector to pursue.

Large	5420	1934-84	£60-£70	$70-$80	_____	_____	☐
Small	5527	1935-84	£35-£40	$50-$60	_____	2 5	☐
Miniature	6046	1939-84	£30-£35	$40-$50	_____	_____	☐
Tiny	6144	1940-60	£55-£65	$115-$125	_____	_____	☐
Limited edition for Higbees							
Large	6761	1986	£110-£120	$250-$300	_____	_____	☐
Small	6791	1967-91	£30-£40	$60-$70	_____	_____	☐

Old King Cole Designer H. Fenton
Early versions have a yellow crown and grey white hair, there is also a difference in the pleats of the collar, as shown in the photograph.

Large	6036	1939-60	£140-£160	$275-$300	_____	_____	☐
Small	6037	1939-60	£70-£80	$100-$120	_____	_____	☐
Lge yellow Crown		1938-39	£2200-£2800	$6000-$7000	_____	_____	☐
Sml yellow Crown		1938-39	£1700-£2000	$4000-$5000	_____	_____	☐
RDICC exclusive							
Tiny	6871	1990	£20-£30	$60-$70	_____	_____	☐

Old Salt Designer G. Sharpe

Portraying an old sea dog The large colourway with its very limited run is seen by many collectors as a good investment for the future.

Large	6782	1987-90	£50-£60	$90-$110	_____	_____	☐
Miniature	6557	1984-91	£15-£20	$40-$50	_____	_____	☐
Prototype	6657	1984	£300-£500	$500-$700	_____	_____	☐

Othello Designer M. Abberley

From the Shakespearian collection.

Large	6673	1982-89	£65-£75	$100-$120	_____	_____	☐

Paddy Designer H. Fenton

Depicts an Irishman from old English ballads and songs.

Large	5753	1937-60	£75-£85	$140-$160	_____	_____	☐
Small	5768	1937-60	£40-£45	$65-$75	_____	3 5	☐
Miniature	6042	1939-60	£35-£40	$50-$60	_____	_____	☐
Tiny	6145	1940-60	£55-£65	$115-$125	_____	_____	☐

Parson Brown Designer C. J. Noke

Some versions have green hats while others are brown.

Large	5486	1935-60	£75-£85	$150-$170	_____	_____	☐
Small	5529	1935-60	£40-£45	$70-$80	_____	40	☐

Paul McCartney Designer S. Taylor

Member of the Beatles and the most successful songwriter of all time.

Medium	6724	1984-91	£30-£35	$80-$100	_____	_____	☐

Pearly Boy Designer H. Fenton

An early version of 'Arry.

Brown
Large		1947	£600-£800	$1200-$1400	_____	_____	☐
Small		1947	£150-£175	$400-$500	_____	_____	☐
Miniature		1947	£100-£150	$500-$600	_____	_____	☐

Blue Tentative values only, an exceptionally rare jug
Large		1947	£4500-£6000	$8000-$9000	_____	_____	☐
Small		1947	£1500-£2000	$4000-$4500	_____	_____	☐

Pearly Girl Designer H. Fenton

An early version of 'Arriet.

This piece is so rare that its value is difficult to estimate, however a small size sold for $6000 in the USA in 1986 and a large size sold for $25000 in 1987. £2000 would be a good price for a small version and £6000 for the large in 1991. A colour variation with a brown jacket is known to exist.

Pearly King Designer S. Taylor

The Cockney Pearly King, (see Pearly Queen)

Large	6760	1987-91	£50-£60	$90-$110	_____	_____	☐
Small	6844	1990-91	£25-£30	$45-$55	_____	_____	☐

Pearly Queen Designer S. Taylor

A reworking of the 'Arry and the 'Arriet theme. The Cockney Pearly Button Queen.

Large	6759	1987-91	£50-£60	$90-$110	_____	_____	☐
Small	6843	1990-91	£25-£30	$45-$55	_____	_____	☐

Pendle Witch Designer A. Faulds

The start of the Myths Fantasies and Legends series by Kevin Francis. A limited edition of 5000 with only 3000 made.

Large	6826	1989-91	£70-£80	$150-$170	_____	_____	☐

Pied Piper Designer G. Blower

The historical basis of this legend is much disputed, but it has been attributed to the bubonic plague of the seventeenth century which affected both rats and children.

" 'Come in,' said the mayor, looking bigger,
And in did come the strangest figure..."

From the poem by Browning.

Large	6403	1954-80	£50-£60	$75-$85	_____	_____	☐
Small	6462	1957-80	£40-£45	$40-$50	_____	৪ ০	☐
Miniature	6514	1960-80	£30-£35	$30-$40	_____	_____	☐

Poacher Designer M. Henk

This jug is still in the current range. The large size was issued in a colourway listed below.

Large	6781	1987-90	£50-£60	$90-$110	_____	_____	☐
Miniature	6515	1960-91	£15-£20	$45-$50	_____	_____	☐

Pied Piper

Poacher

North American Indian

Paddy

Pearly Girl

Pearly Boy

Porthos Designer M. Henk
One of the Three Musketeers

Large	6440	1956-91	£45-£55	$95-$110		
Small	6453	1956-91	£25-£30	$50-$65		2-0
Miniature	6516	1960-91	£15-£20	$40-$50		
Large	6828	1988 Commission	£60-£70	$100-$120		

The Postman Designer Stan Taylor
A sold out edition of 5000 from the Lawleys by Post "Journey through Britain".

Small	6801	1988	£70-£80	$110-$130	

Punch and Judy Man* Designer D. Biggs
The colours on Punch are reversed in early versions.

Large	6590	1964-69	£260-£300	$550-$600	
Small	6593	1964-69	£150-£170	$380-$425	
Miniature	6596	1964-69	£150-£170	$380-$425	

Queen Elizabeth I Designer W. Harper
Limited edition of 9500, commissioned by Lawleys by Post to celebrate the 400th anniversary of the Armada.

Small	6821	1988	£30-£40	$80-$90	

Queen Victoria
A special edition (No. 6788) colourway of 3,000 for the Retail China Guild, which was subsequently released for general distribution.

Large	6788	1987	£60-£70	$200-$220	
Large	6816	1989-91	£45-£50	$90-$100	

The Red Queen Designer W. Harper
Part of the Alice in Wonderland series. "Off with their heads."

Large	6777	1988-91	£50-£60	$100-$120	
Small	6859	1990-91	£30-£35	$55-$65	
Miniature	6860	1990-91	£20-£25	$50-$60	

*Also found in bone china

Regency Beau Designer D. Biggs

George Bryan Brummell 1778-1840, known as "Beau Brummell" and "undisputed monarch of the mode". He was famed for his social presence and wit and his artistry in dress, particularly his perfectly tied cravats and freshly laundered shirts. In 1816, gambling debts forced him to flee to France and he died in obscurity in the Asylum of the Bon Savreu, in Caen.

A few small versions have grey eyebrows instead of brown.

Large	6559	1962-67	£475-£525	$850-$950	_____	_____	☐
Small	6562	1962-67	£275-£325	$500-$550	_____	_____	☐
Miniature	6565	1962-67	£300-£350	$600-$750	_____	_____	☐

Ringo Starr Designer Stan Taylor
The drummer with the Beatles.

Medium	6726	1984-91	£30-£35	$80-$100	_____	_____	☐

Rip van Wrinkle* Designer G. Blower
The man who slept for 20 years from the novel by Washington Irving in 1820.

Miniature	6517	1960-91	£15-£20	$40-$55	_____	_____	☐

Robin Hood (First Version) Designer H. Fenton
The hero from the medieval legend romanticised as having robbed from the rich to give to the poor. Reputed to have been Robin of Locksley in the 12th Century.

Large	6205	1947-60	£70-£80	$145-$155	_____	_____	☐
Small	6234	1947-60	£40-£50	$75-$85	_____	_____	☐
Miniature	6252	1947-60	£40-£45	$70-$80	_____	_____	☐.

Robin Hood (Second Version) Designer M. Henk

Miniature	6541	1960-91	£15-£200	$40-$50	_____	_____	☐

Robinson Crusoe* Designer M. Henk
"It happened one day, about noon, going towards my boat, I was exceedingly surprised with the print of a man's naked foot on the shore, which was very plain to be seen in the sand. I stood like one thunderstruck, as if I had seen an apparition."

Daniel Defoe's story was seen by Karl Marx as a parable of Bourgeois capitalism!

Large	6532	1960-82	£55-£65	$80-$90	_____	_____	☐
Small	6539	1964-82	£30-£35	$45-$55	_____	3 0	☐
Miniature	6546	1964-82	£25-£30	$40-$50	_____	_____	☐

*Also found in bone china

Romeo Designer D. Biggs

From the Shakespearian collection. A number of handle variations are known to exist.

Large	6670	1983-89	£65-£75	$100-$120	_____	_____	☐

Ronald Reagan Designer E. Griffiths

Former Hollywood actor and President of the USA.

"I get pretty tired of people knocking Hollywood. It's a nice town — and its not true that movie folk are unfriendly to those who make less money."

An edition of 2000. Now sold out. Originally offered as a limited edition of 5000 it failed to sell well and the remaining jugs were sold by the Republican Party to a USA dealer.

Large	6718	1984	£220-£250	$300-$350	_____	_____	☐

Sairey Gamp* Designers L. Harradine & H. Fenton

A dubious midwife in Dickens' Life and Adventures of Martin Chuzzlewit. A fat old woman with a husky voice, and a moist eye... She wore a very rusty black gown, rather the worse for snuff, and a shawl and bonnet to correspond. "Also partial to the bottle, she has an imaginary friend, Mrs Harris."

The longest 'running' Doulton character jug produced continuously for 51 years.

Large	5451	1935-86	£55-£65	$70-$85	_____	_____	☐
Small	5528	1935-86	£30-£35	$40-$50	_____	_25_	☐
Miniature	6045	1939-86	£30-£35	$30-$40	_____	_____	☐
Tiny	6146	1940-60	£55-£65	$100-$115	_____	_____	☐
Limited edition colourways for Strawbridge and Clothier							
Large	6770	1986	£150-£200	$250-$300	_____	_____	☐
Small	6789	1987	£60-£70	$90-$110	_____	_____	☐

Samuel Johnson Designer H. Fenton

England's 'first' man of letters, the compiler of the English language and the first hack journalist — in short the founder of all the newspapers and first proper dictionary of the English language and the first hack journalist — in short the founder of all the newspapers and current affairs programmes. A man who had every confidence in his knowledge and ability to instruct the world about literature and art, but suffered a life long doubt about himself and God. A truly humble man but imbued with a fundamental sense of goodness and common sense.

Large	6289	1950-60	£150-£170	$250-$300	_____	_____	☐
Small	6296	1950-60	£75-£95	$180-$200	_____	_____	☐

Samson and Delilah Designer S. Taylor

Large	6787	1988-91	£65-£75	$130-$150	_____	_____	☐

Punch and Judy Man

Robin Hood

Porthos

Ronald Reagan

Rip van Winkle

Red Queen

124

Sam Weller Designers L. Harradine & H. Fenton
Mr Pickwick's loyal servant in *The Pickwick Papers*.

"Wery glad to see you, indeed, and hope our acquaintance may be a long 'un, as the gen'l'm'n said to the fi'pun'note."

The small size version has the handle at the back and slightly different features.

Large	6064	1940-60	£70-£80	$140-$150	_____	_____	☐
Intermediate	5841	1938-48	£85-£95	$180-$200	_____	_____	☐
Small	5841	1948-60	£38-£42	$75-$85	_____	_____	☐
Miniature	6140	1940-60	£35-£40	$60-$70	_____	_____	☐
Tiny	6147	1940-60	£60-£70	$115-$125	_____	_____	☐

Sancho Panca* Designer G. Blower
The faithful squire of Don Quixote, 'El Caballero de la Triste Figura' The Knight of the Mournful Countenance in the novel by Cervantes.

Some versions have a pink bridle on the handle compared to the normal brown colour.

Large	6456	1957-82	£55-£65	$80-$90	_____	_____	☐
Small	6461	1957-82	£30-£35	$50-$60	_____	_____	☐
Miniature	6518	1960-82	£25-£30	$40-$50	_____	_____	☐

Santa Anna & Davy Crockett
Number 3 in the Antagonists Collection. Not yet sold out.

Large	6729	1985	£65-£70	$140-$150	_____	_____	☐

Santa Claus (First Version)
Good old Father Christmas.

Issued with several different handle variations.

Doll	6668	1981	£55-£65	$80-$90	_____	_____	☐
Reindeer	6675	1982	£50-£60	$65-$85	_____	_____	☐
Sack of Toys	6690	1983	£50-£60	$65-$85	_____	_____	☐

Santa Claus (Second Version)

Holly Leaf	6794	1987	£150-£160	$300-$350	_____	_____	☐
Candy Cane	6793	1987	£300-£350	$800-$1000	_____	_____	☐
Candy Cane	6840	1989	£80-£100	$150-$200	_____	_____	☐
Special edition for RDICC and USA							
Holly Leaf Mini	6900	1991	£20-£25	$30-$40	_____	_____	☐

*Also found in bone china

Santa Claus (Plain Handle)

Miniature	6706	1960-91	£15-£20	$40-$50	_____	☐

Scaramouche (First Version) Designer M. Henk

A character in the Pan-European folk theatre, the Commedia dell' Arte. Scaramouche, always dressed in black, is an insuppressible braggart who boasts of a noble origin, alleged riches and his abilities and refinements as a lover. Always conniving, he was able to make defeat seem like victory. His was often a satirical role in the improvised dramas.

Large	6558	1962-67	£350-£400	$575-$600	_____	_____	☐
Small	6561	1962-67	£225-£250	$450-$500	_____	_____	☐
Miniature	6564	1962-67	£175-£200	$450-$500	_____	_____	☐
Large	6774	1987	£70-£90	$150-$200	_____	_____	☐

Scaramouche (Second Edition) Designer G. Blower

A reworked second version of this medieval European. First issued in a special edition of 1500 (6774) through the UK Retail Guild.

Large	6774	1987	£90-£210	$180-$200	_____	_____	☐
Large	6814	1988-91	£45-£55	$90-$110	_____	_____	☐

Simon the Cellarer Designers C J. Noke & H. Fenton

A wine-cellarer from a 19th century drinking song and from the look of him a real boozer.

Large	5504	1935-60	£75-£85	$130-$150	_____		☐
Small	5616	1936-60	£40-£45	$65-$75	_____	4 5	☐

Simple Simon Designer G. Blower

A character from the rhyme of the same name, the complete village idiot.

Large	6374	1953-60	£240-£275	$475-$525	_____	☐

Sir Henry Doulton Designer E. Griffiths

Available to Collector Club Members only.

Small	6703	1984	£60-£80	$80-$100	_____	6 5	☐

Sir Thomas More Designer S. Taylor

The Lord Chancellor to Henry VIII who was beheaded in 1535 for refusing to swear a oath of supremacy which went against his Catholic beliefs. He was canonised by the Catholic church in 1935.

Large	6792	1988-91	£50-£60	$100-$120	_____	☐

Sleuth Designer A. Moore
A portrayal of that famous detective Sherlock Holmes.

Miniature	6639	1973-91	£15-£20	$40-$50	_____	_____	☐

Smuggler* Designer D. Biggs
Another eighteenth century British character, a traditional tax dodger.

Large	6616	1968-80	£55-£65	$80-$90	_____	_____	☐
Small	6619	1968-80	£30-£35	$50-$60	_____	30	☐

Smuts Designer H. Fenton
South African Statesman, General, lawyer, philosopher, botanist and Chancellor of Cambridge University.

"But my dear lady, I am only a general in my spare time" — reply to an American botanist surprised to learn that Smuts was an authority on grasses. Though sophisticated and hardworking he was misunderstood and was unpopular with his people.

Large	6198	1946-48	£600-£800	$1200-$1400	_____	_____	☐

St. George* Designer M. Henk
The patron saint of England. As an officer in the Roman Army, George criticised the Emperor Diocletian for persecuting Christians. He was tortured and beheaded in 303 A.D. but was defiantly cheerful to the end. His martyrdom has thus become a symbol of successful combat against evil — hence the legend of the slayer of the dragon and the rescue of Lady Truth.

Large	6618	1968-75	£100-£120	$180-$200	_____	_____	☐
Small	6621	1968-75	£80-£90	$140-$160	_____	_____	☐

Tam O'Shanter Designer M. Henk
The central character of a poem by Robert Burns who considered it one of his best works. Composed sometime around 1790, it is said to have been the work of a single day. Burns composed much of his poetry while out walking or riding and his wife remembered him "crooning to himsel" when on a walk at this time.

"The night drave on wi' sangs and clatter
And aye the ale was growing better
The landlady and Tom grew gracious
wi' favours secret, sweet and precious."

Early versions have a distinctly ridged blue hat as compared to the lighter blue, smooth later version.

Large	6632	1973-79	£55-£65	$95-$100	_____	_____	☐
Small	6636	1973-79	£35-£40	$40-$50	_____	30	☐
Miniature	6640	1973-79	£30-£35	$40-$50	_____	_____	☐

Sancho Panca

Sleuth

Scaramouche (First Version)

Tam O'Shanter

Santa Anna and Davy Crockett

Santa Claus

Toby Philpots* Designer C. J. Noke

Later versions have a plain blue scarf with no dots.

Large	5736	1937-69	£75-£85	$120-$140			☐
Small	5737	1937-69	£40-£45	$70-$80		_3 0_	☐
Miniature	6043	1939-69	£35-£40	$45-$55			☐

Tony Weller Designers L. Harradine & H. Fenton

The father of Sam Weller in the *Pickwick Papers*.

"His face had expanded under the influence of good living — and its bold fleshy curves had so far extended beyond the limits originally assigned them that unless you took a full view of his countenance in front, it was difficult to distinguish more than the extreme tip of a very rubicund nose."

Twice married, he warns: Be very careful o' vidders all your life."

Extra Large		1936-42	£120-£140	$270-$290		_40_	☐
Large	5531	1942-60	£70-£80	$140-$150			☐
Small	5530	1935-60	£40-£45	$80-$90		_35_	☐
Miniature	6044	1939-60	£35-£40	$60-$70			☐

Touchstone Designer C. J. Noke

A clown in Shakespeare's *As You Like It*.

Large	5613	1936-60	£110-£130	$200-$225			☐

Town Crier (First Version)* Designer D. Biggs

A medieval news announcer who was impossible to switch off.

Large	6530	1960-73	£100-£120	$200-$230			☐
Small	6537	1960-73	£75-£90	$150-$190			☐
Miniature	6544	1960-73	£80-£90	$130-$150			☐

Trapper* Designers M. Henk & D. Biggs

An early North American fur hunter. *On some Centennial Jugs the snow shoe strings are painted black instead of white and the main part of the horn is grey as compared to light brown.*

Large	6609	1967-82	£55-£65	$80-$100			☐
Small	6612	1967-82	£35-£40	$45-$55		_10_	☐
Miniature	Pilot	1967-68	£700-£1100	$1800-$2000			☐

Large Centennial Backstamp

Large	6609	1967	£90-£110	$180-$220			☐

Ugly Duchess* Designer M. Henk

The irritable duchess from *Alice in Wonderland*. "If everybody minded their own business," said the Duchess in a hoarse growl, the world would go round a deal faster than it does."

A small version has been found with a yellow/orange headband jewel as compared to the normal red.

Large	6599	1965-73	£225-£250	$350-$400	_____	_____	☐
Small	6603	1965-73	£150-£175	$250-$300	_____	_____	☐
Miniature	6607	1965-73	£140-£160	$250-$300	_____	_____	☐

Uncle Tom Cobbleigh Designer M. Henk

A character from an eighteenth century ballad, Widdicombe Fair. It relates how Tom Pearse's mare, which he had lent to some friends, dies on the way to Widdicombe fair, in Devon, but remains, as a ghost, to haunt the road.

Early versions have pure white hair.

Large	6337	1952-60	£170-£190	$375-$425	_____	_____	☐

Veteran Motorist Designer D. Biggs

A character representing one of the first motorists. One whose value has risen steadily in the last 12 months.

Large	6633	1973-83	£60-£70	$100-$120	_____	_____	☐
Small	6637	1973-83	£35-£45	$60-$70	_____	3 0	☐
Miniature	6641	1973-83	£30-£40	$35-$45	_____	_____	☐

Vicar of Bray Designers C. J. Noke & H. Fenton

From an eighteenth century song satirising the trimmers of the Church of England who changed their opinions to suit the political climate.

"Old principles I did revoke,
Set conscience at a distance,
Passive obedience is a joke,
A jest is non-resistance.
And this is law, I will maintain
Unto my dying day, Sir,
I will be Vicar of Bray, Sir!"

Some versions have a distinct yellow rim around the hat.

Large	5615	1936-60	£90-£110	$190-$210	_____	_____	☐

*Also found in bone china

Viking Designer M. Henk

A Scandinavian explorer/warrior. With such a limited production run this jug is seen by many as a good investment.

Large	6496	1959-75	£90-£100	$160-$180	_____	_____	☐
Small	6502	1959-75	£60-£70	$80-$100	_____	40	☐
Miniature	6526	1960-75	£60-£80	$120-$140	_____	_____	☐

Walrus and Carpenter* Designer M. Henk

From *Alice Through the Looking Glass* 1872. The Walrus and the Carpenter invite some young oysters for a walk along the shore, and proceed to eat them:

"'It seems a shame,' the Walrus said,
'To play them such a trick
After we've brought them out so far,
And made them trot so quick!'
The carpenter said nothing but
'The butter's spread too thick!'"

Large	6600	1965-79	£65-£75	$100-$120	_____	_____	☐
Small	6604	1965-79	£40-£45	$60-$70	_____	_____	☐
Miniature	6608	1965-79	£30-£35	$40-$50	_____	_____	☐

W. C. Fields Designer D. Biggs

It's a funny old world a man's lucky if he gets out of it alive."

Large	6674	1983-85	£55-£65	$90-$100	_____	_____	☐

Wild Bill Hickock Designer Michael Abberley

From the Wild West Series

Medium	6736	1985-89	£45-£50	$80-$90	_____	_____	☐

William Shakespeare Designer M. Abberley

The Great Bard 1564-1616. The most popular and acclaimed of the classical playwrights. Though strangely enough there is very little information recorded about him and continuous controversy regarding the actual authenticity of a few of his works.

Large	6689	1983-91	£45-£55	$90-$110	_____	_____	☐

Winston Churchill (Second Version) Designer S. Taylor

Character jug of the year 1992. Only available for 12 months.

Large	6907	1992	£65-£75	$95-$105	_____	_____	☐

Witch Designer S. Taylor

The old witch of legend and superstitious times seen here with her cat supposedly her familiar and source of her link with the devil. With a production run of only six months this jug is set to prove popular amongst collectors.

Large	6893	1991	£85-£95	$180-$200			☐

Wyatt Earp

From the Wild West Series

Medium	6711	1985-89	£45-£50	$80-$90			☐

Yachtsman (First Version)* Designer D. Biggs

Commemorates the achievements of Sir Francis Chichester 1901-72, air pioneer and long distance yachtsman. In 1960, he was the winner of the first single-handed Transatlantic Yacht Race. In 1966/7 he made the first solo navigation of the world via the Capes of Good Hope, Leeuwin and Horn. He took 226 days to cover 29,600 miles. He was knighted by the Queen on his return to Plymouth.

Large	6622	1971-79	£70-£80	$100-$120			☐
Small	Pilot	1971	£1500-£2000	$3000-$4000			☐
Miniature	Pilot	1971	£1500-£2000	$3000-$4000			☐

Yachtsman (Second Version) Designer S. Taylor

A backstamp release of 750 was produced for the first Canadian Doulton Fair at Durham in 1988.

Large	6820	1989-91	£50-£60	$90-$110			☐

Walrus and Carpenter

Wyatt Earp

The Old Tinies

Auld Mac	D6257	1947-1960	£90-£100	$230-$250
John Peel	D6259	1947-1960	£90-£110	$240-$260
Cardinal	D6258	1947-1960	£80-£90	$230-$250
Mr Pickwick	D6260	1947-1960	£85-£90	$210-$230
'Arry	D6255	1947-1960	£80-£95	$190-$210
'Arriet	D6256	1947-1960	£80-£95	$190-$210
Mr Micawber	D6143	1940-1960	£55-£65	$130-$140
Sam Weller	D6147	1940-1960	£60-£70	$115-$125
Fat Boy	D6142	1940-1960	£55-£65	$130-$140
Old Charley	D6144	1940-1960	£50-£60	$90-$110
Paddy	D6145	1940-1960	£50-£60	$90-$110
Sairey Gamp	D6146	1940-1960	£50-£60	$90-$110

The original 12 tinies

The modern tinies

The Modern Tinies

These jugs are the same size as the "Old Tinies" 1½ inches tall and only twelve characters have been produced. They were sold by subscription at a rate of one a month ending in December 1982. Originally sold at £12.50 sterling they are valued now on the British market at £15-£20 each and $30-$40 on the American market. The Dickens jug is considered the rarest and does bring a slight premium. The reason for such an increase is their relative scarcity on the market as few collectors are willing to part with their own collection.

The following characters were made.

Character		Designer
Mr Bumble	D6686	Robert Tabbenor
Fagin	D6679	Robert Tabbenor
Uriah Heep	D6682	Robert Tabbenor
Mrs Bardell	D6687	Robert Tabbenor
Oliver Twist	D6677	Robert Tabbenor
Betsy Trotwood	D6685	Michael Abberley
Bill Sykes	D6684	Michael Abberley
Scrooge	D6683	Michael Abberley
David Copperfield	D6680	Michael Abberley
Little Nell	D6681	Michael Abberley
Artful Dodger	D6678	Peter Gee
Dickens	D6688	Eric J Griffiths

Full Modern Tinies Set   £250-£275 $300-$325

The Latest Tinies

The Doulton Collectors Club have released two new tiny characters, the Beefeater and Old King Cole. Both have proved very popular and are now much in demand. Value around £25 each.

A new set of Tinies was commissioned and modelled in the early 1980s. They never made it to production stage as they were rejected by the marketing department.

The Tiny Old King Cole and Tiny Beefeater

Doulton Toby Jugs

Doulton Toby Jugs, which in recent years have been overshadowed by the interest in character jugs, are likewise collected by enthusiasts worldwide.

Many Doulton character jugs are represented in Doulton Toby form as well. One character jug which causes disappointment to those who don't realise that it comes in two forms is the Winston Churchill. Only a few white Churchill character jugs exist compared with the thousands of Toby Churchills produced and sold worldwide. Following an article in the *Daily Mail* where the Winston Churchill Toby Jug was mistakenly referred to as being worth £5000, hundreds of people phoned the paper and major auction houses in the mistaken belief that they possessed a valuable jug.

1992 could herald the start of an attempt by Royal Doulton to develop their current range. All the current Toby jugs have been withdrawn. A new small size jug entitled The Jester has been released in an edition of 2500. It will be interesting to note the progress of this release, it could well be the start of future releases.

Current Toby Jug

Medium size
The Jester — Limited Edition 2500

George Robey and Charlie Chaplin

Doultonville Tobies

Mr Litigate	D6699	1983-91	£20-£25 / $35-$40
Miss Nostrum	D6700	1983-91	£20-£35 / $35-$40
Mr Furrow	D6701	1983-89	£35-£40 / $70-$80
Rev Cassock	D6702	1983-90	£30-£35 / $60-$65
Mr Tonsil	D6713	1984-91	£20-£25 / $35-$40
Madame Crystal	D6714	1984-89	£35-£40 / $70-$80
Mrs Loan	D6715	1984-90	£35-£40 / $70-$80
Betty Bitters	D6715	1984-90	£30-£35 / $60-$65
Sergeant Peeler	D6720	1985-91	£20-£25 / $35-$40
Captain Salt	D6712	1985-91	£20-£25 / $35-$40
Miss Studious	D6722	1985-89	£35-£40 / $70-$80
Dr Pulse	D6723	1985-91	£20-£25 / $35-$40
Albert Sagger	D6745	1986	£55-£60 / $120-$130
Major Green	D6740	1986-91	£20-£25 / $35-$40
Mike Mineral	D6741	1986-90	£30-£35 / $60-$65
Fred Fly	D6742	1986-91	£20-£25 / $35-$40
Mr Brisket	D6743	1986-91	£20-£25 / $35-$40
Alderman Mace	D6766	1987-91	£20-£25 / $35-$40
Floria Fuchsia	D6767	1987-90	£30-£35 / $60-$65
Charlie Cheer	D6768	1987-91	£20-£25 / $35-$40
Monsieur Chasseur	D6769	1989-91	£20-£25 / $35-$40
Fred Fearless	D6809	1989-91	£20-£25 / $35-$40
Len Lifebelt	D6811	1989-91	£20-£25 / $35-$40
Captain Prop	D6812	1989-91	£20-£25 / $35-$40
Pat Parcel	D6813	1989-91	£20-£25 / $35-$40

Top row: Albert Sagger, Miss Nostrum; Bottom row: Betty Bitters, Rev Cassock

Discontinued Toby Jugs

Character		Production Dates	Size		
Best is not too good	D6107	1939-60	4½ "	£120-£140	$250-$275
Captain Cuttle	D6266	1948-60	4½ "	£90-£100	$175-$190
Charlie Chaplin		1919	11"	£2000-£2500	$6000-$7000
Double XX	D6088	1939-69	6½ "	£150-£175	$300-$350
Falstaff	D6063	1939-91	5¼ "	£30-£40	$50-$60
Falstaff	D6062	1939-91	8½ "	£40-£50	$80-$90
Fat Boy	D6264	1948-60	4½ "	£90-£100	$175-$190
George Robey		1920	10½ "	£2000-£2500	$6000-$7000
Happy John	D6069	1939-91	5½ "	£40-£50	$70-$80
Happy John	D6031	1939-91	8¾ "	£45-£55	$80-$90
Honest Measure	D6108	1939-91	4½ "	£30-£40	$40-$50
Huntsman	D6320	1950-91	7½ "	£35-£45	$90-$95
Jolly Toby	D6109	1939-91	6½ "	£40-£50	$80-$90
Mr Micawber	D6262	1948-60	4½ "	£90-£100	$175-$190
Mr Pickwick	D6261	1948-60	4½ "	£90-£100	$175-$190
Old Charley	D6069	1939-60	5½ "	£60-£80	$175-$190
Old Charley	D6030	1939-60	8¾ "	£110-£130	$225-$250
Sairey Gamp	D6263	1948-60	4½ "	£90-£100	$175-$190
Sam Weller	D6265	1948-60	4½ "	£90-£100	$175-$190
Sherlock Holmes	D6661	1981-91	8¾ "	£40-£50	$90-$100
Sir Francis Drake	D6660	1981-91	9"	£40-£50	$90-$100
Sir Winston Churchill	D6171	1941-91	9"	£50-£60	$90-$100
Sir Winston Churchill	D6172	1941-91	5½ "	£40-£50	$60-$70
Sir Winston Churchill	D6175	1941-91	4"	£30-£40	$40-$50
The Squire	D6319	1950-69	6"	£140-£160	$215-$300

Winston Churchill

Cliff Cornell Toby Jug

These jugs were produced in 1956 for an American industrialist called Cliff Cornell. They were used as gifts to his friends and customers. In all versions of the jug the base carries the following inscription;

Greetings Cliff Cornell Famous Cornell Fluxes Cleveland Flux Company

The jugs were produced in three colours brown, blue and tan and in two sizes, 9 inches and 5½ inches. The tan version is considerably rarer than the brown and blue versions. The production run for the brown and blue jugs has been reported as being 500 jugs for each large version and 375 for each of the smaller versions. Production figures for the tan variations are unknown but are certainly far lower.

Market Value:

	Brown		Blue		Tan	
Large	£240-£260	$295-$325	£240-£260	$295-$325	£450-£500	$500-$525
Small	£220-£240	$300-$350	£220-£240	$300-$325	Unknown	

A pilot colour version of this jug has been found in Southern California. It is a large size Blue Cliff Cornell with an A mark backstamp. Colour differences are: the grey hat has no black band around it, the necktie is green with red dots rather than red with white dots and the shoes are brown instead of black.

Cliff Cornell

Early Huntsman

In 1963 an early Huntsman with a silver rim and different colours on the body was found. It was dated for 1919 nearly twenty years prior to the current Huntsman introductions. This jug was sold in auction for £300 in 1983. Its value on today's market would be considerably more.

Kingsware Huntsman

This jug was designed by Harry Fenton and produced at Burslem from 1910. Its actual production lifetime is unknown but it must have been for a good few years as examples turn up regularly on the market. Its price range is £200-£300/$225-$275. A silver rim version of this jug has been found. Its value would be considerably higher.

Charrington

This 9¼ inch Toby was made in 1934 to advertise Charrington Ale. It was previously thought that only two versions existed; however, the Collectors' Club have, in the last year, identified a third version. The three versions are identifiable by differences in the wording on the front and side of the jug. The newly discovered version says 'Toby' on the front and just 'Charrington' on the side. The other two common versions say 'Toby Ale' in block letters on one and 'One Toby leads to Another' in script on the other.

Market Value:
Common versions: £80-£90/$300-$350 Rare versions: £200-£250/$700-$800

The Three Charrington Tobies

George Robey

An extremely rare early Doulton Toby made during the 1920s. It has a cover in the form of a hat, the absence of which would reduce its market value.
Market Value:
£2000-£2500/$6000-$7000

Charlie Chaplin

Another extremely rare early Doulton Toby made during the 1920s. It also has a cover in the form of a hat.
Market Value:
£2000-£2500/$6000-$7000

John Wesley

Designed by Charles Noke in the 1920s only two prototypes were believed to have been made. A stern looking jug featuring a methodist preacher, the jug would bring over £5000 if another example were discovered.

Kingsware Squire

A forerunner to the 1950s Squire produced in the early part of the century. Worth approximately £400.

John Wesley

Ordinary and Kingsware Squire

Miscellaneous Wares

From the 1930s through to the 1950s Royal Doulton produced a range of derivatives of Character Jug characters, from teapots to bookends. The Dickens characters, such as Tony Weller, were very popular but the war years significantly affected their production, some of them being discontinued after 1942. All derivatives are far more scarce than their Character Jug counterparts and they are keenly collected.

This scarcity is a result of their low production numbers and their vulnerability to damage in use. In the last year prices on average increased by 10 per cent and in some cases, such as teapots, values moved ahead strongly. Given their scarcity and relative cheapness, prices should continue to grow in this section.

Mr Pickwick and Sairey Gamp Bookends

Bookends

Very similar to the napkin rings, these are 4" high Dickens busts mounted on wooden bases. They were produced between 1934 and 1939. Once again these are very rare and they bring in a high price on the market. There are only four characters in the set.

HN1615	Mr Micawber	£800-£1200	$2000-$3000
HN1616	Tony Wellor	£800-£1200	$2000-$3000
HN1623	Mr Pickwick	£800-£1200	$2000-$3000
HN1625	Sairey Gamp	£800-£1200	$2000-$3000

Tobacco Jars

These are large jugs manufactured with a metal insert in the top to house the cover mechanism. There were only two characters made between 1938 and 1960.

D5844	Old Charley	£500-£800	$3000-$4000
D5854	Paddy	£500-£800	$3000-$4000

Miniature Sugars

Sometimes referred to as toothpick holders, these look like slightly expanded miniature Character Jugs that are missing their handles. Only three characters were made between 1940 and 1941. Whilst not as valuable as other derivatives they are eagerly collected and consequently difficult to obtain.

D 6150	Sairey Gamp	£250-£300	$800-$900
D 6151	Paddy	£250-£300	$1000-$1200
D 6152	Old Charley	£250-£300	$1000-$1200

Sugar Bowls

Standing about 2½" in height these are wider versions of the miniature sugars. They were only produced in 1939 and are highly sought after.

D 6011	Sairey Gamp	£250-£300	$800-$1000
D 6012	Old Charley	£300-£350	$1000-$1200
D 6103	Tony Weller	£300-£350	$1000-$1200

Teapots

All of these were made in 1939 and discontinued with the outbreak of the Second World War. They are quite rare and are avidly collected, Old Charley being slightly rarer than the other two.

Old Charley is known to exist in two colour versions. The more frequent colouring comprises a chocolate brown overcoat, rose waistcoat, rust brown hair, blue-dotted white bow-tie and a pale yellow light in the lantern. In the lesser known version he wears a rust brown overcoat, yellow waistcoat, chocolate brown hat, blue striped white tie, darker yellow in the lantern and grey hair. The black lantern and brown buttons remain common to each style.

Additional colourways for Tony Weller exist.

D6015	Sairey Gamp	£600-£800	$2000-$2500
D6016	Tony Weller	£600-£800	$2500-$3000
D6017	Old Charley	£800-£1000	$2500-$3000

(Rarer version would be worth slightly more)

In 1988 the Collectors Club revived character teapots by commissioning Old Salt D6818 which now sells for £80/$120. The following year three more teapots were added to the general range, Falstaff, Long John Silver and Old Balloon Seller and these are still in production today.

Old Charley and Jester wall vases

Wall Vases

Known either as wall vases or wall pockets, only two characters were produced, although the Jester has two versions known. Both were produced between 1939 and 1941. They are rarer than the teapots but have a similar market value.

D6110	Old Charley	£850-£1000	$4000-$5000
D6111	The Jester	£850-£1000	$4000-$5000

Whisky Decanters

Two figural whisky decanters with detachable heads were produced with a wooden tantalus for Asprey and Company of Bond Street, London in the 1930s. These are very rare and the only examples to turn up this year brought £3500 at Louis Taylors Auction House, Stoke-on-Trent. The value on the American market would be in excess of $8000.

Napkin Rings

These were made between 1939 and 1960 mainly for the USA market. They rarely appear on the UK market and only seldom on the USA market. Looking like mini busts set on porcelain napkin rings they were only made in six Dickens' characters and occasionally turn up in a presentation box of 4 or 6.

M59	Fat Boy	£200-£220	$450-$550
M58	Mr Micawber	£200-£220	$400-$500
M57	Mr Pickwick	£200-£220	$400-$500
M62	Sairey Gamp	£200-£220	$450-$550
M61	Sam Weller	£200-£220	$400-$500
M60	Tony Weller	£200-£220	$400-$500
Full Boxed Set		£1800-£2000	$3000-$3500

Extra Large Size

The only reported jug of this size is Tony Weller. It is approximately one inch higher than the large size Tony Weller and noticeably wider at the top.

Market Value: £120-£150 $225-$250

Mini-Busts

These are a series of busts manufactured between 1939 and 1960. Only six characters were manufactured, all of which are Dickens' characters. They were made with both square and oval bases.

	Character	Market Value	
D6048	Buz Fuz	£45-£55	$80-$90
D6050	Mr Micawber	£45-£55	$80-$90
D6049	Mr Pickwick	£45-£55	$80-$90
D6047	Sairey Gamp	£45-£55	$80-$90
D6052	Sam Weller	£45-£55	$80-$90
D6051	Tony Weller	£45-£55	$80-$90

Liqueur Containers

These are small size jugs, whose tops have a small round opening for cork stoppers. The presence of their original contents will increase the price of this jug. Commissioned in the 1960s for the firm of Walklate Ltd.

Falstaff	£45-£55	$80-$100
Poacher	£45-£55	$80-$100
Rip Van Winkle	£45-£55	$80-$100

Ashtrays

These are miniature jugs whose bases are attached to a black bowl. There were only four characters used and they have no difference in market value between them. All were made between 1936 and 1960.

D5601	Dick Turpin	£70-£90	$110-$130
D5602	John Barleycorn	£70-£90	$110-$130
D5599	Old Charley	£70-£90	$110-$130
D5600	Parson Brown	£70-£90	$110-$130

Dickens Jugs and Tankards

These six jugs and one tankard, while not strictly speaking character jugs, are derivatives and are collected by jug enthusiasts. They all have a raised relief which depicts various Dickens' characters and scenes.

Old London	1949-60	£90-£110	$270-$300
Peggotty	1944-60	£90-£110	$270-$300
Old Curiosity Shop	1935-60	£60-£80	$130-$150
Pickwick Papers	1937-60	£60-£80	$130-$150
Oliver Twist	1936-60	£60-£80	$130-$150
Oliver Asks for More	1949-60	£70-£90	$250-$270
Oliver Twist Tankard	1949-60	£70-£90	$250-$270

Ash Pots/Ash Bowls

These are small character jugs with an internally overhanging top lid. This top lid may have one or two grooves in it to rest cigarettes. They were all made between 1939 and 1960.

D6006	Auld Mac	£70-£90	$110-130
D6007	Farmer John	£70-£90	$110-130
D5925	Old Charley	£70-£90	$100-125
D5926	Paddy £70-£90	$100-125	
D6008	Parson Brown	£70-£90	$100-125
D6009	Sairey Gamp	£70-£90	$110-130

Musical Character Jugs

These are large character jugs with a musical box and key built into their base. When wound and lifted off a surface they will play a tune. They are believed to have been made between 1938 and 1945; although their production would have been curtailed by World War Two.

	Character	Tune Played	Market Value	
D5889	Auld Mac	The Campbells are Coming	£400-£500	$750-$8850
D5858	Old Charley	Have a Health to His Majesty	£450-£550	$750-$850
D6014	Old King Cole	Old King Cole Was A Merry Old Soul	£1300-£1600	$4000-$5000
		Yellow Crown Old King Cole	£2000-£2500	$8000-$10000
D5887	Paddy	An Irish Jig	£400-£500	$800-$1000
D5833	Tony Weller	Come Landlord Fill the Flowing Bowl	£400-£500	$750-$850

Cigarette Lighters

These were first produced by Royal Doulton in 1958 and only 14 characters in a small size were used. Prior to this a company in America, Van Cleff Studios who had a Doulton dealership converted some small character jugs into lighters. This was done by filling them with plaster of paris, painting it black and inserting a lighter mechanism in the top. These converted jugs are not listed in this booklet and the following list only lists those made by Royal Doulton.

D6505	Bacchus	1964-74	£70-£80	$140-$160
D6233	Beefeater	1967-74	£70-£80	$120-$140
D5838	Buz Fuz	1958-59	£90-£120	$200-$225
D6506	Captain Ahab	1964-74	£70-£80	$140-$150
D5842	Captain Cuttle	1958-59	£110-£120	$200-$225
D6385	Falstaff	1958-74	£70-£80	$190-$210
D6504	Lawyer	1962-74	£70-£80	$200-$225
D6386	Long John Silver	1958-73	£70-£80	$110-$120
D5843	Mr Micawber	1958-59	£90-£120	$200-$225
D5839	Mr Pickwick	1958-62	£80-£100	$190-$210
D6453	Musketeer Porthos	1958-59	£200-£250	$425-$475
D5527	Old Charley	1958-74	£65-£75	$110-$120
D6464	Poacher	1958-74	£70-£80	$110-$120
D6463	Rip Van Winkle	1958	£200-£250	$425-$475
	Pilot Granny	?	Value impossible to determine	

Old Charley in all his variations. This is one of the most popular characters ever released by Royal Doulton. In constant production from 1934-1984 over 15 different derivatives were produced. The total number of actual jugs made must be in the tens of thousands

Beswick Character and Toby Jugs

The first Beswick character jug, Tony Weller, was introduced in 1935 and other Dickens personalities soon followed. During the war some patriotic character jugs were produced, promoting the endeavours of the army, navy and airforce. These are now amongst the most desirable.

The Beswick character jugs had all been withdrawn by 1973. Today the Beswick studio, as part of the Royal Doulton group, are responsible for the production of all the character and toby jugs with a Royal all the character and toby jugs with a Royal Doulton backstamp.

The market value of all Beswick Jugs has risen in the last two years as Doulton collectors discover this relatively inexpensive collecting area.

Tony Weller

Betsy Trotwood

Scrooge

Toby Philpot in both sizes with the Midshipman

Barnaby Rudge

Cap Cuttle

Martin Chuzzlewit

Little Nells Grandfather

Henry VIII

Falstaff

Beswick Character and Toby Jugs Market Values

Model No	Name of Model	Height	Modeller	Design	Withdrawn Date	Market By Values
281	Tony Weller CJ	6¾″	Mr Watkin	1935	1973	£40-£50
		Re-modelled				£45-£55
310	Mr Micawber CJ	8¼″	Mr Watkin	1935	1973	£40-£50
		Re-modelled				£45-£55
371	Sairey Gamp CJ	6½″	Mr Watkin	1936	1973	£40-£50
372	Scrooge CJ	7″	Mr Watkin	1936	1973	£40-£50
575	Laurel & Hardy cruet	4½″	Mr Watkin	1938	1969	£35-£40
673	Tony Weller (sugar)	2¾ ″	Mr Watkin	1939	1973	£22-£27
674	Mr Micawber (cream)	3¼″	Mr Watkin	1939	1973	£22-£27
689	Sairey Gamp pepper noted in 2 colour schemes	2½″	Mr Watkin	1939	1973	£22-£27
690	Mr Micawber salt	3½″	Mr Watkin	1939	1973	£22-£27
691	Sairey Gamp yeapot	5¾″	Mr Watkin	1939	1973	£88-£99
735	Old Bill CJ		Mr Watkin	1939	1954	£150-£175
736	Navy		Mr Watkin	1939	1954	£150-£175
737	Air Force		Mr Watkin	1939	1954	£150-£175
931	Winston Churchill TJ	7″	Mr Watkin	1941	1954	£250-£300
1110	Toby Phillpot TJ	8″	Mr Gredington	1948	1973	£88-£99
1111	Toby Phillpot TJ	6½″	Mr Gredington	1948	1973	£77-£88
1112	Midshipman Toby TJ	5¼″	Mr Gredington	1948	1973	£125-£150
1113	Martha Gunn (holding jug) TJ	3½″	Mr Gredington	1948	1966	£150-£175
1114	Toby Sitting on Barrel (holding jug) TJ	3½″	Mr Gredington	1948	1966	£150-£175
1116	Peggoty teapot	6″	Mr Gredington	1948	1973	£77-£99
1117	Pecksniff (cream) CJ	3½″	Mr Gredington	1948	1973	£30-£35
1118	Pickwick (sugar)	3″	Mr Gredington	1948	1973	£30-£35
1119	Pickwick cream CJ	3¼″	Mr Gredington	1948	1973	£30-£35
1120	Captain Cuttle CJ	4½″	Mr Gredington	1948	1969	£55-£77
1121	Barnaby Rudge CJ	4½″	Mr Gredington	1948	1973	£88-£99
1129	Pecksniff (sugar)	3½″	Mr Gredington	1948	1973	£30-£35
1203	Dolly Varden teapot	6¼″	Mr Gredington	1950	1973	£88-£99
1204	Mr Varden (cream) CJ	3½″	Mr Gredington	1950	1973	£30-£35
1205	Mrs Varden (sugar)	3″	Mr Gredington	1950	1973	£30-£35
1206	Sairey Gamp (preserve)	3″	Mr Gredington	1950	1973	£30-£35
1207	Tony Weller preserve	3″	Mr Gredington	1950	1973	£30-£35
1369	Sam Weller teapot	6¼″	Mr Gredington	1955	1973	£88-£110
2030	Martin Chuzzlewit CJ	4¾″	Mr Hallam	1965	1973	£35-£45
2031	Little Nell's Grandfather CJ	5⅜″	Mr Hallam	1965	1973	£88-£110
2032	Mr Bumble CJ	4⅞″	Mr Hallam	1965	1973	£17-£23
2075	Betsy Trotwood CJ	5″	Mr Hallam	1966	1973	£95-£110
2095	Falstaff CJ	6¾″	Mr Hallam	1967	1973	£35-£40
2099	Henry VIII CJ	7″	Mr Hallam	1967	1973	£55-£65

CJ = Character Jug   T = Toby Jug

KEVIN FRANCIS TOBY JUGS

Let me start by by first declaring my interests here. One of the reasons for the long delay between the fourth edition of this book and this edition is the time my partner Francis Salmon and myself have spent in developing our own range of limited edition Toby Jugs. I am totally biased, believing that that these are the finest Toby Jugs ever made, and that their quality will ensure their continued success. The whole thinking behind these jugs is based on our ten years experience with character jug collectors.

We have endeavoured to produce what collectors tell us they want. That is, very high quality production and detailed modelling combined with realistically low edition numbers. The subjects chosen have come in many cases from collectors themselves whilst others have been a reflection of personalities of our time such as President Gorbechov.

Margaret Thatcher

These jugs are marketed under the Kevin Francis backstamp and are produced by studio pottery production methods at the Peggy Davies Studio in Stoke-on-Trent. We are completely independent from Royal Doulton and quite proud of it. Keen collectors, however, will recognise several ex-Doulton modellers such as Peggy Davies, Doug Tootle and Geoff Blower. The connection does not stop there as several of our painters are in fact retired Doulton prestige painters.

We only use the finest materials and highly skilled workers in a production process which owes more to the traditional skills of yesterday than the mass manufacturing production methods of today. Each piece is made by hand and is very complex requiring in some cases 12 part moulds as compared to the four or five used for an ordinary character jug.

Our pottery in Stoke-on-Trent is run by Rhodri Davies, the son of Peggy Davies. Before forming the studios with his mother Rhodri was a production manager at Wedgwood.

To date we have released over 60 characters which, with our policy of having colourways and small size jugs, represents 80 different jugs. Of these releases 15 have sold out or been withdrawn. These discontinued jugs have now started to find their own market and a price structure has developed. It is still very early days and the market is a thin one but early signs are very encouraging.

Our first release was The Vic Toby a limited edition of 1000 named after Vic Schuler, the author of the book British Toby Jugs.

This was followed by several characters reflecting hobbies such as the Gardener and Shareholder by Peggy Davies.

The early death of Peggy Davies in 1989 forced us to expand our modelling base and the last two years have increasingly come to reflect the work of modellers such as Geoff Blower and Doug Tootle. We have expanded the range to include well known personalities of today such as Margaret Thatcher and Pavarotti.

Recent successes have included the series "Great Artists and Potters" where we have portrayed some of the most influential persons from the pottery industry. Releases such as Clarice Cliff and Hannah Barlow have been very successful editions as they are all as low as 350.

The future for Kevin Francis Toby jugs is one we are confident of. The last year has seen the Japanese market starting to take off for us and we are now exporting jugs to Australia and South Africa. The market for our discontinued jugs is growing and several have now doubled in value. We feel that if we can maintain the very high quality of these editions along with low production numbers, demand will continue to increase.

A selection of Kevin Francis Toby and Character Jugs plus The Collector Royal Doulton commissions

Susie Cooper

Salvador Dali

DISCONTINUED/SOLD OUT KEVIN FRANCIS

Character	No Release/ Edition	Market Price	Year Released	Modeller
Blue Vic	700	£175.00	1988	PD
Yellow Vic	300	£200.00	1988	PD
The Cook	250	£150.00	1989	PD
Teddy Bear	250	£250.00	1990	AM
Clarice Cliff	350	£450.00	1990	DT
Polka M Thatcher	200	£150.00	1989	DT\PD
Tribute M Thatcher	100	£150.00	1990	DT\PD
Green Shareholder	300	£125.00	1989	PD
White Churchill	600	£150.00	1989	PD
Green Doctor	200	£125.00	1989	PD
Yellow Gardener	350	£125.00	1989	PD
Pavarotti Figure	250	£175.00	1990	DT
Faded Montgomery	100	£150.00	1990	DT
White Little Vic	250	£60.00	1989	PD
Grey St Churchill	750	£150.00	1990	DT
Blue St Churchill	750	£150.00	1990	DT
Hannah Barlow	350	£300.00	1991	DT
David Winter	900	£400.00	1991	DT
Blue Shareholder	1500	£100.00	1989	PD
Red Gardener	1500	£100.00	1989	PD
Blue Doctor	500	£100.00	1988	PD
Postman	1500	£100.00	1988	PD
Little Teddy ShowSpecial	95	£60.00	1991	AM
Susie Cooper	350	£200.00	1991	DT

OTHER WARE

Fanztec Vase	100	£120.00	1989	JM
Reindeer Boy	50		1992	AM
Lady with Fan	500	£125	1992	GB

CURRENT KEVIN FRANCIS INTRODUCTIONS

Blue Little Vic	2500		1989	PD
Black Churchill	5000		1989	PD
Blue Churchill	5000		1989	PD
Red Clown	1500		1989	GB
White Clown	1500		1989	GB
Black Clown	1500		1989	GB
Santa	1000		1989	GB
Blue Mrs Thatcher	1000		1989	DT

Brown Golfer	1000	1990	AM
Blue Golfer	1000	1990	AM
Violet Queen Mother	900	1990	DT
Pink Queen Mother	900	1990	DT
L Blue Shakespeare	1000	1990	GB
D Blue Shakespeare	1000	1990	GB
President Gorbechov	1000	1990	AM
Grey Pavarotti	500	1990	DT
Black Pavarotti	1500	1990	DT
Douglas Bader	750	1990	AM
Blue Fisherman	500	1990	GB
Green Fisherman	500	1990	GB
Pope John Paul	250	1990	DT
Montomgery	750	1990	DT
Blue Hearty G Fellow	750	1990	DT
Green Heart G Fellow	750	1990	DT
Brindle Bulldog	500	1990	AM
White Bulldog	500	1990	AM
Charlotte Rhead	350	1991	DT
Little Teddy	2500	1991	AM
Blue Little Winston	2500	1991	PD
Black Little Winston	2500	1991	PD
Field Marshall Rommel	750	1991	DT
Henry VIII	750	1991	GB
Little Clarice	2500	1991	DT
Little Gorby	2500	1991	AM
Helmut Kohl	999	1991	AM
Stormin Norman	750	1991	AM
Pershore Miller	1500	1991	RN
Little Golfer	2500	1991	AM
General Patton	750	1991	AM
Josiah Wedgwood	350	1991	DT
William Moorcroft	350	1991	DT
Boris Yeltsin	250	1991	AM
John Major CJ	500	1991	RN
Stormin Norman CJ	1000	1991	RN
Margaret Thatcher	650	1991	SI
Miniature Teddy	2500	1991	AM
Princess Diana	900	1992	DT
Sir Henry Doulton	350	1992	DT
Salvador Dali	350	1992	AM
John Major	650	1992	SI
Neil Kinnock	650	1992	SI

Queen Elizabeth II	400	1992	DT
Moe Weiderman	350	1992	AM
Sandra Kuck	550	1992	DT
General Eisenhower	750	1992	AM
John F Kennedy	750	1992	HS
Picasso	350	1992	AM

PD = Peggy Davies
DT = Douglas V Tootle
GB = Geoff Blower
AM = Andrew Moss
RN = Ray Noble
SI = Spitting Image
JM = John Martin
HS = Harry Sachs

Recommended Reading

Character Jugs
Royal Doulton Character and Toby Jugs by Desmond Eyles
Character Jug Collecting by Syd Gardner
A Revised Price Guide to the Royal Doulton Discontinued Character Jugs by Princess and Barry Weiss
Collecting Royal Doulton Character & Toby Jugs by Jocelyn Lukins
British Toby Jugs by Vic Schuler

Other Doulton Works
Royal Doulton Series Ware by Louise Irvine
Limited Edition Loving Cups and Jugs by Richard Dennis
Royal Doulton Figures by Desmond Eyles, Richard Dennis and Louise Irvine
The Doulton Story by Paul Atterbury and Louise Irvine
Doulton Flambe Animals by Jocelyn Lukins
Royal Doulton Figures by Charlton Press
The Doulton Lambeth Wares by Desmond Eyles
The Price Guide to the Complete Royal Doulton Figurine Collection by Mary Lou Yeager
The Lyle Price Guide To Doulton by Mick Yewman
Phillips Guide to Doulton by Catherine Braithwaite
Doulton Animals by Jocelyn Lukins

By the same author

The Doulton Figures Collectors Handbook by Kevin Pearson
Available direct from the publishers.

Royal Doulton Restorations

PROFESSIONAL REPAIRS OF YOUR FIGURINES — CHARACTER & TOBY JUGS LAMBETH — BURSLEM — KINGSWARE STONEWARE — FLAMBE — ETC

Restorations by
Ronald L. Aiello
Judy G. Aiello

Ronald L. Aiello

1313 Mt Holly Rd, Burlington

New Jersey 08016, USA

1-609-387-2587

1992 CHARACTER JUG OF THE YEAR

WINSTON CHURCHILL

£75.00 UK $125.00 USA

This superb new character jug will only be available during 1992. Production will cease in December 1992. To ensure you reserve an example contact either our UK or our USA office. Access Mastercard and Visa accepted with Telephone orders.

Kevin Francis

Landcroft House

85 Landcroft Road

East Dulwich

London SE22 9JS

Tel 081 693 3688

Fax 081 299 1513

Kevin Francis

32246 Oakview

Warren

Michigan 48092

Tel 313 795 8360

Fax 313 795 3884

UK International Ceramics Ltd
proudly present

General Eisenhower

A large size character jug exclusively produced for us by Royal Doulton.

No 3 in the series of the Great Generals Collection.

Special world-wide edition of 1000

Available December 1992

General De Gaulle

A large size character jug exclusively produced for us by Royal Doulton.

No 4 in the series of the Great Generals Collection.

Special world-wide edition of 1000

Available May 1993

**Also available: Yellow Falstaff Limited Edition 1500
John Shorter Limited Edition 1500**

For full details and order forms please write to:

Mrs Barbara Groome, Product Manager, UK International Ceramics, 10 Wilford Bridge Spur, Melton, Woodbridge, Suffolk, England IP12 1RJ

Tel: 0394 386662 Fax: 0394 386742

Collecting Doulton
THE UK NATIONAL & INTERNATIONAL MAGAZINE FOR COLLECTORS OF BOTH OLD & NEW DOULTON POTTERY.

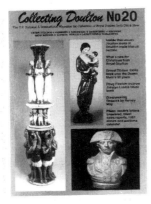

Whether you collect
CHARACTER JUGS
KINGSWARE
EARLY SALT GLAZE
ADVERTISING ITEMS
SERIESWARE
FIGURINES
BUNNYKINS
ANIMALS or FLAMBÉ
You **need** Collecting Doulton

It contains **more** news than any other magazine and is issued six times a year to an enthusiastic **worldwide** readership. Contains news on upcoming Shows & Auctions, plus reports afterwards. Also covers news from around the world, letters answered by Jocelyn Lukins, **FREE** classified adverts, comprehensive book service. Also regular feature articles & what's new!

EVERYTHING YOU NEED TO KEEP IN TOUCH

6 magazines per year. UK – £12 post paid.
Overseas:- USA – £18 International Money Order or $36 **CASH** or $42 personal cheque. Aus – £20 International Money Order or $48 **CASH** or $56 personal cheque.
AVOID TIME & TAKE OUT A 2 or 3 yr HASSLE FREE SUBSCRIPTION - avoid price rises too!

SUBSCRIBE WITHOUT DELAY TODAY

Detach here

✂ ---

COLLECTING DOULTON Subscription form
Please print clearly in block capitals

I enclose .... for 1 yr, 2 yrs, 3 yrs subscription.

Name ....
Address ....
....
....

VISA 🔲 No ....

Exp date ....

Send **with remittance** to:- Collecting Doulton, 2 Strafford Avenue, Elsecar, Nr Barnsley, S Yorkshire, S74 8AA. Tel 0226 745156.

THE SMALL COLLECTOR

WORLD WIDE SPECIAL EDITION OF 1500 ONLY

NEVER TO BE REPEATED OR RE RELEASED IN A DIFFERENT COLOURWAY

Produced by Royal Doulton for Kevin Francis after a design by Geoff Blower the small Collector is a stunning character jug. With such a low edition size the jug is proving very popular, to reserve your collector contact Kevin Francis at either our American or British office.

UK

£55.00

U.S.A.

$125.00

KEVIN FRANCIS
85 LANDCROFT ROAD
EAST DULWICH
LONDON SE22 9JS

Tel 081 693 3688

Fax 081 299 1513

KEVIN FRANCIS
32246 OAKVIEW
WARREN
MICHIGAN 48092

Tel 313 795 8360

Fax 313 795 3884

ALL PRICES INCLUDE POSTAGE AND PACKING TEL AND FAX ORDERS ACCEPTED WITH CREDIT CARDS.